Tnuasach

About the Author

Martin Towey is an Irish-born author living in a village on the east coast of Scotland. A neurological physiotherapist by profession, he has always loved writing since a small boy. His short stories are mostly historical fiction but he has also written a stress management booklet. His last book *An Act of Madness*, has recently been adapted for the stage.

Cnuasach

Echoes of an Irish childhood

Martin Towey

EVENTISPRESS

A CIP catalogue record for this title is available from the British Library.

ISBN: 978-1-7393286-0-3

Published by Eventispress in 2023

Printed by PODW

Dedication

This book is dedicated to my lovely mum and dad.

Nuala and Danny Towey

Contents

Acknowledgements

I WOULD LIKE to thank my family for encouraging me to write, especially my father, who always showed an interest in my writing even when I was a youngster. Mrs Burga Monaghan, my one-hundred-and-four-year-old surrogate granny, has been honest and loving in her advice and encouragement. Also, my friend and editor, Suella Holland at Forsaken Ireland, who went through my writing with a fine toothcomb. To my friends in Ireland, Scotland, and other far-flung places, who have read and critiqued this anthology. Many thanks to my wonderful publisher Diana Diggins at Eventispress who is always so encouraging. I am indebted to Grace Vaughan at Sky Daddy Media, an inspiring creative writing teacher, whose honesty and passion helped me cross the finish line with my first short story many years ago now. Go raibh míle maith agat to artist Noreen Walshe, who generously permitted me to use her beautiful painting 'The Lark Ascending' for the front cover. To Margaret Rabbitte, whose kindness to me as a small child, will never be forgotten. To my secondary school English teacher, Anne Boyle, who fostered my love of literature. To all those people and experiences which inspired the writings in this book. Final thanks to my beautiful mum, a voracious reader herself, from whom I received my love of the written word.

Preface

CNUASACH IS AN old Irish word meaning 'collection' or 'anthology'. This book is a collection of short stories and poems that I have written over several years, which I now realise reflect key events that have shaped me to become the person that I am. Some of the stories are light-hearted and darkly humorous, while others I suspect will pull on the old heart strings. It is a memoir for the most part with obvious exceptions.

The first story, *The Lark and the Hare*, relates to the illustration on the cover of the book, and is an allegory for the journey that I have made so far in life. Like the hare lost in the grass, I spent most of my adolescent years looking in all the wrong places for safety, love and acceptance, believing for way too long that I was an outsider, a misfit on the fringes of a minority. The sudden death of my beautiful mother to suicide was a turning point in my life. The kindness of good friends, the love and support of my family, and working on myself, have all helped me to accept myself as I get through the darker times. Education, occupation and love have all been kind to me, each having helped me to develop into a better human being with a healthier perspective on life than I might otherwise have. Like the lark soaring high in a vast, blue sky,

I can see what was once obscured, and consider my life as one enriched by experience.

Throughout it, writing has brought me to a better, more considered understanding of myself and others. Whether reading the work of a great writer or poet or putting my own thoughts and feelings down on paper, the written word has clarified confusion, put old ghosts to rest and brought a healing to my heart. Writing also brings out the quirky part of me that lurks beneath and helps me to slowly reveal an identity worthy of revelation.

The Lark and the Hare

ON THAT FINAL morning, his mother had seen him to the door of their little form, put her paws around him and gently kissed the fur between his ears. Both of them did their best not to cry. She beamed at him, her eyes moist with motherly affection, 'and mind those foxes whatever you do, they're divils'. She hugged him again. '*Amach leat*' ('Off with you'). His mother's command of Harish was pretty limited but she was always one for the dramatics. He beamed at her. 'Okay, mammy, I'll do my best' and so off he went down the leafy path, sniffing the scents of the foliage surrounding him. The urge to run back to her was overwhelming but he knew that would just make things harder. He daren't look back but instead literally put one paw in front of the other, feeling a profound sadness he had never before experienced. He would be brave. Everything would work out. He tightened the satchel on his back and kept going. He knew his mother would be feeling just as he did, resisting the impulse to bound after him, but every leveret had to do this, to leave the family form. It was just the way of things in Animal Kingdom. He pushed onwards and told himself that he would be ok and he would return, one day, to Swallow's Dip bringing with him enough supplies to support his parents and the little ones for a lifetime.

Within a few hours, he had long since crossed the stream which bordered the woods where he used to play as a tiny leveret. With a mixture of utter fascination and unrelenting heartache, he explored and sniffed the moss-strewn path in the direction of Faraway Meadow, a place Grandfather Hare had often spoken of. A leveret had so much to learn and apparently this was the place to do just that, to make something of oneself. His beloved grandfather had most probably followed this very same path all those years ago. He had met Hamish's grandmother in Faraway Meadow, not that long after leaving the family form. It gave Hamish some comfort to think that he was not the first of his down to make an expedition from Swallow's Dip and he, just like his grandfather, would make a life for himself, learn about Great Earth, find a means of survival and who knows, perhaps even find the jack of his dreams. In Swallow's Dip, no one but Great Grandmother Hare had seemed to notice how his head would be turned by a handsome jack who had wandered into their territory from some far-off land. 'Love is love, young Hamish, remember that. It comes in all shapes and sizes and the thing about love is, it is a force for good. It is as necessary as grass, as fundamental as fresh water'. 'Without love, a hare may as well give himself up to a fox' she would say, her little paws knitting frantically 'give himself up to a fox.' she would repeat to herself, her little fingers faster than a furious flea. She had long since passed into the Unknown Frontier but he felt her presence often, especially when he called on her. A spirit like hers could never cease to exist.

Thoughts of Great Grandmother Hare filled him with a stillness, one which was a balm to his heart. *All would be well.* So it was, that Hamish Hare, with all this thinking and without his knowledge, had passed more milestones in one day than even his grandfather before him. By sunset, he had found a cosy spot in a thicket of smooth meadow grass and within a short spell, he had closed his tired eyelids and fell, in no time at all, into a dream where he was back in Swallow's Dip amongst his down. He could see them all there, sitting by a sun-streaked stream, his mother, his father, aunts and uncles, siblings and cousins, Grandfather Hare, Grandmother Hare and even Great Grandmother Hare. It was she, however, who looked up from her knitting and with a look of panic in her old eyes, shouted 'Wake up Hamish, wake up!' Suddenly he awoke in an altogether different landscape, with a feeling of intense fear, in a land that looked unrecognisably different from the one where he had fallen asleep only a few hours before. A large moon now shone overhead and every blade of grass, every twig, branch and trunk appeared etched in silver. High up above, he saw something move swiftly and almost imperceptibly. *Was that a bird?* he asked himself out loud. And this was the first mistake of many that Hamish Hare would make on his journey. He had drawn attention to himself. He knew with every follicle of fur that something was watching him. He could feel eyes upon him.

A rustling from a hawthorn bush brought into view a pair of eyes. 'Hello there'. Hamish shook like a leaf, his mouth dry, his teeth beginning to chatter. 'I said, hello there, little one. Are you lost? You're not from around these parts, are you? I know every squirrel and frog this side of High Forest. What brings a leveret like you, to a place like this?' Apart from the eyes, all that he could make out was a set of very sharp teeth, glinting in silver moonlight from the dark hawthorn. 'Come, come. Don't be shy, little leveret. I am a friend.' With that the unmistakeable form of a large fox, tiptoed her way in his direction. Without a second thought, Hamish surprised the fox by darting directly towards her and right under her body between her front and hind legs. His mother's warning to keep clear of 'those foxes' rang through his brain as his paws found a speed, of which he could only have dreamt until now. He sprung with an agility that not even the fittest of the other leverets of his down could have mustered. Within minutes, he was a great distance from where he had encountered the fox. Miraculously he had escaped, but he knew that it had been just pure luck on this occasion. He might not be so fortunate the next time. It was perhaps, less about his agility and more the fact that this particular fox was of the lazier variety.

In a short time, he was able to slow his pace and meander more leisurely through the moonlit countryside. On his way, he saw a squirrel who lifted his cap acknowledging him with a friendly nod, throwing a nut his way. 'Thank you, Mr. Squirrel'. *Yes indeed*, he thought, *there are good sorts around.* An hour or so later, as he took a moment to stare at the reflection of the moon in a still pond, a little frog ribbited, stuck out her tongue, producing a little centipede she had been keeping for her tea. She motioned for Hamish to help himself. 'Thank you very much little frog, but you see I'm a vegetarian.' The frog looked perplexed, if a little offended, but then smiled and hopped off. *She's only a baby frog, so I suppose she's probably not familiar with Harish ways, he* surmised. *It was still a nice gesture*, he thought to himself.

Daydreaming, as was his habit, Hamish soon found himself in less favourable terrain, a marshy landscape, interspersed with bracken and patches of coarse grass. He decided to plough on however. This was most likely the Grasses of Confusion that Grandad Hare used to speak of. *At least I'm on the right path,* he thought to himself. Soon, however, he felt a bit panicky and decided to try and get beyond the Grasses of Confusion as soon as he could. There was just something unnerving about the place. As he quickened his pace, he found that, in order to avoid large clumps of thorny bracken, he had to deviate from any type of direct path. Scurrying this way and that, he soon found himself forcing his way through thicker and darker undergrowth and was aware of water gurgling somewhere close by. The coarse grass he was now negotiating was getting denser by the second. It was nothing like the sweet, soft variety of home. The whole place had a nightmarish quality. It seemed to him that these grasses were knowingly positioning themselves so that their hardened stems pointed and pricked his soft pelt. In a state of escalating panic, pain, and disorientation, Hamish found he couldn't actually see his surroundings for the undergrowth was dense and seemed to close in around his small frame. He winced as his front paws sank painfully into a small hole under foot. Down a long narrow burrow, he tumbled.

Coming to a halt, all was quiet. This stillness was but momentary. He became aware that there was movement some distance ahead of him, further down the tunnel. Moments later, he could hear an aggressive squeaking. Whatever was down here ahead of him was not a friend. He had heard this noise before. *River rats*, he thought. Frantically, he pushed his hind paws into the earth behind him, his front paws into the earth on either side. Slowly, somehow, he managed to turn himself and with every muscle fibre in his short legs, he propelled himself out of the hole into a lesser darkness. Not willing to encounter his aggressive pursuers, he fought his way through the lance-like grasses for what seemed like an eternity, when suddenly he emerged from the scrubland.

A meadow stretched out before him, blanketed in a beautiful, silver moonlight. He stopped and got his breath, but was keenly aware that he was still on the outskirts of enemy territory, so he ran for his life towards a hill in the far distance. Soon he was scampering up its steep slope, upon which a majestic, ancient tree stood proudly like an old warrior. Surrounding its broad base, long inviting grass made for the perfect hideout for a hare who was far, far from home. Scurrying through the biting cold, he reached the tree and instinctively lay his pulsing body flat to the ground, ears flat on his back. Motionless, Hamish could feel his heart beating against the cold earth below, his breath urgent and sharp in his windpipe. He closed his eyes momentarily, his mind racing.

When he opened them again, he felt a huge sense of relief, in the knowledge that he could see for miles around and knew that it was unlikely he would be seen here amongst the tall grass. This sense of relief was short-lived however, when he heard a soft whisper from above 'Little one, are you ok?' His heart lunged forwards in his chest in fright, a shrill shriek of alarm punctured the cold night air. It had come from the depths of his little body. 'It's okay little one'. Drawing his body tighter to the ground, Hamish made himself as small as possible, but he knew it was futile. He would still be visible to his unseen observer. His head swivelled low, this way and that, in fast jerky movements. 'Up here, little one'. Lifting his eyes towards the vast moon, hovering by a swaying branch, he was now looking at what appeared to be the silhouette of a bird, dwarfed black against the large, all-seeing moon. 'Don't be frightened little Hare. You're a courageous one. You have done well for such a novice explorer. So much learning in just one day.' His instincts told him that this small bird was not a threat. So, finding courage from within, he cleared his throat and began. 'Who are you and how do you know of my journey? Have you been following me?' 'I have little one. I've been keeping an eye on you. I am your skylark and you, my fine friend, are a clever little leveret, do you know that? You outsmarted that old fox and she's a wily one! You got lost in the Grasses of Confusion and yet you outsmarted them also. Your mother would be proud of you.'

He thought of his mother and this filled him with love and now, for the first time since leaving her embrace that morning, he felt his little body relax. His muscles eased and he sat up on his front paws, looking up at the kindly face of the old lark, who was now sitting on a nearby branch like a wise old thing. 'It pained me, little one, to see you from above, lost in the dark grasses, confused, alone and unsure, but through your own determination and wit, you overcame all the challenges and fears you faced. Great Earth, little leveret, is without doubt, a frightening place at times. There will be wily old foxes who will try to entrap you, unseen earthy pits, down which you may tumble, and paths which entice, but bring hardship and heartache. Despite this, if you draw upon your own wisdom, you will survive. And you have done just that, this very day. You, little one, found this lofty old tree on top of this ancient hill. Many a leveret would have been the makings of a fox's dinner this day but, you, you survived Hamish Hare'. Hamish sat perplexed. 'How do you know my name?' The lark sat quietly on her branch for some moments, the great moon behind her, in its silver magnificence. 'Do not ponder on such matters. Just know that you are loved, even from afar. There will be dark days on your journey when all seems lost, but there will be wondrous moments too and great adventures ahead. Of course, there will be times when you will

feel utterly forsaken and alone, but around the next hedge, or stream, you will find friendship. And, like every living creature, the love you seek deep in your heart, will find you, because it is already in you. It dwells in every breathing creature on Great Earth. It is of our choosing, whether we look for it to find it.'

The lark, flew down to a branch a little closer to Hamish. In a whisper, the lark turned her crested head towards him. 'Remember what I told you, long, long ago. Love is love and as necessary as grass, as fundamental as fresh water. Without love, a hare may as well give himself up to a fox.... may as well give himself up for a fox'. And with that, the lark took flight, sweeping heavenward into the moonlit sky as a little hare sat far, far below on a frosted moonlit meadow, left utterly bewildered but entirely comforted.

In no time at all, Hamish had found a cosy spot at the base of the kindly, old tree and shaped a little form in the soft grass. His eyes heavy with tiredness, he felt safe and snug. Tumbling gently into sleep, he dreamt that he himself was flying high in the night sky. Swooping low over the frosted fields, he began to make out far off on the horizon, a tinge of most beautiful orange. The first rays of early morning filled him with joy as he dived and swerved over the now golden-hued grasses. From this great height, he could see so much of Great Earth, its long rivers and meandering streams, and woods. He even saw the wily old fox, who looked up at him in confusion and agitation. Not far ahead were the Grasses of Confusion. He saw all of this and beyond. Flying over the fields and woods of Swallow's Dip, he soon swooped over his mother's home, landing on the little window sill next to her bedroom. He hopped from the window sill onto the floor and made his way with his delicate little bird feet to where she lay. Sound asleep, his mother snored gently. Perched on her pillow, he whispered into her ear 'All is well mother and will be well'. His soft wings gently caressed the side of her face, her whiskers twitching. The little bird then took flight and flew away in the direction of the kindly old moon.

In his slumber, Hamish Hare, sighed contentedly to himself, as the sun covered the frosted fields of Great Earth with morning light.

Memories of St. Patrick

MEMORIES OF ST. PATRICK'S DAY for many growing up in Ireland in the late 70s and early 80s are precious, etched delicately into grey matter like detailed, intricate designs adorning the standing stones of our ancient past. Perhaps it is my mind playing tricks on me, but when I was growing up, every St. Patrick's Day began in glorious spring sunshine. There was always a Sunday feeling about it, a day of rest and peace. The roads were quiet, the sky was expansive and empty, apart from the odd jet of a plane bringing people to and from our small island. As a child, on that day, I didn't want to be anywhere else but standing at the top of the lane leading down to the road from the farm. It seemed so long down to the road back then. Long to a small boy with short steps, but in reality, it was 'only a hen's trot', as my dad would say. St. Patrick's morning always seemed to be a 'fresh' day, an Irishism, if ever there was one. This freshness signalled that this was a special day, and the fields always seemed to bask in a gentle, clear morning light. I recall sheep, too, munching away placidly in the fields opposite the house. At a very young age, I had a fascination with St. Patrick himself, particularly his image. Enjoying my own company, I remember dressing up as him, but not in any jokey way but assuming the role of the great man himself. I don't recall exactly what I wore, but I remember having something on my head befitting a mitre, holding a staff of sorts (probably an old stick), and wearing something resembling a cape or cloak. I stood tall, well, as tall as a seven-year-old could, and walked gracefully, imagining the crowds parting in adoration of my saintly ways. 'Delusions of grandeur or wha'?' I felt very holy and sanctimonious and secretly believed that perhaps I was destined for greatness, ecumenically speaking of course.

Heading to mass with my older brother, sister and my parents, I did not, however, don the cape or mitre. In our best 'Sunday going to mass clothes', before we set off, we children would be given little badges of green, white and gold, but worn with most pride was our little poesy of shamrock, pinned to our lapels. Heading off to our little country parish church, at this tender age, I felt like the bees' knees. The sun would shine down on us after the mass, as we all stood outside the church door and met our distant neighbours and friends. There was an atmosphere of friendship, peace and hope. I am not sure exactly how the rest of the day would normally play out, but it is a precious memory, standing there squinting and smiling in the sunshine of a St. Patrick's morning with my mother, beautifully turned out in a green knitted cardigan and dress, her auburn hair and her beautiful smile radiant, like the sun pouring down from above. I felt safe, at peace. Life was good.

Now, so many years later, on a day that the sun's corona is obscured by clouds and the world uncertain as a pandemic of the same name ravages her way across the globe, we are comforted by something not even a deadly virus can strip us of, that is our common humanity. There may be no shamrock or ribbon for me, and my beautiful mother may be long gone from this troubled world, but deep within us, our mutual love and care of each other, our awareness of each other will get us through this grey, uncertain time. I can be grateful to my parents for the beautiful memory of childhood innocence that is indelibly etched into my mind. When I am a frail old man, I see myself closing my eyes and remembering the simple joys of boyhood on a St. Patrick's morning, in an Ireland many years past. It is these little treasure chests that we can bring with us in our hearts, that nothing can destroy.

Visiting the Relations

MY MOTHER USED to say, *'you were born in a hurry, and you've been in a hurry ever since'*. Thinking about that now, it's pretty spot on and something I need to manage. It's probably why I need to be mindful in life, because my tendency is towards haste. Anyway, it was with haste and no warning that I came into this world. I was born at home on the farm, my father delivering me into the world. I know he had lots of experiences with delivering calves but welcoming a ginger-headed little human one August morning in 1975 must have been a bit of a shocker for him.

When I remember my childhood, I remember being a happy child. I loved the farm as it all felt so big to me…even though it probably wasn't at all. I used to love going off exploring the fields, the ditches, and streams. I remember having my favourite tree in an old orchard. It wasn't a fancy farm; probably a bit run-down. Not wishing to criticise my father, but it was all a bit chaotic; bits and bobs everywhere. I didn't care though. What I really loved about the place was the space and freedom and my recollection is of bright, fresh days where I could just head off. I don't remember playing with my siblings much as a child. I think we were all pretty independent of each other in terms of play; however, I do remember making huts with my sister, Olive. Poor old Seán, my brother, was always left out of it, as himself and Olive just didn't get on. He was the middle child and the poor little fella acted up as a result and was even less popular with his big sister. I adored Olive and felt I could rely on her to be there. It was her bedroom I'd go to after watching *The Incredible Hulk*, scared out of my wits when I was very small. I'd sleep in her bed. Seán and I shared a room. I remember there was wallpaper with horses jumping over fences. I thought it was creepy. Lying in bed, I loved listening to the wood pigeons in the dusk light. Interestingly, in recent years, Olive remarked that when she hears wood pigeons call, it reminds her of the farm where we grew up. We had a lovely old man called Jackie, who worked with my father on the farm. I loved him and any excuse I would be out with him. I think my most idyllic memory was going down the fields at haymaking time, with a tray of tea and probably scones for 'the men'. I can still smell the hay, the lovely evening sun, the big sky, and yellow-butter fields that seemed to stretch on forever.

Old pals. Me and Bobby Joe ca. 1983

As my mother remarked, I was my brother Seán's 'lap dog' or 'go-for', in the sense that I just did what he asked of me. I would stand with my foot at the bottom of the ladder for what seemed like hours, while he climbed up to the shed roof in mischief, or help him light a fire in the hay shed, which then went out of control. It wasn't out of love or allegiance that I took on this role, but I was kind of afraid of him, not in the sense that he'd hurt me physically, but he was moody and I think I would do anything to prevent him from upsetting my mother. He was always up to devilment. When he wasn't trying to start the tractor, he was playing Evil Kinevil on his bike, jumping over home-made dodgy ramps etc. He was, I can see now, simply being a typical little boy, testing boundaries and exploring. I was a far more cautious child, not really taking chances, happy just to disappear off on my own and explore and get lost down the fields in my daydreams. I was very quiet and didn't speak much until I was a teenager. So muted was I that my mother brought me to the doctor, as she thought I had a hearing problem, given that I wasn't particularly talkative.

My mother was great in the kitchen and there was always home-made bread, apple tarts *et cetera*. People always say they remember my mother's cooking. It was always a warm, welcoming house. I loved it when we had visitors, because mum and dad were always in good form and at their best. Mum was a born entertainer and dad had a knack for telling jokes. There always seemed a strained atmosphere when we were just on our own. It was like we had difficulty relating as a family unit, but on a one-to-one basis we got on well. My mother had, what I assume they would diagnose today as, clinical depression. She was an incredibly loving and sensitive person, but was unknowingly hilarious too. She was extremely selfless, to her own detriment. I don't remember her getting angry, but what was much more damaging was the self-blame and loathing she would direct at herself. Her thinking became distorted, saying, for example that she was a 'bad' mother. She was anything but, and I loved and still love her so much. I feel emotional as I write. Emotional because as one person so close to my heart once explained, she and I were 'cut from the same cloth'. I felt this incredible bond with her. I felt that I understood her. She was part of me and I her. She would confide in me even when I was a young child. Although I probably enjoyed this role, I recognise now, as an adult, that it probably was not healthy for a seven-year-old to be counsellor to someone who was in emotional pain and whose thinking was sometimes distorted. From my birth to when I was about six, my mother was hospitalised on several occasions for months at a time. I don't really recall these episodes, but have vague memories of being a baby-sat at strange houses. It is difficult to write this and I am finding I feel almost nauseous as I put pen to paper. I think of my childhood in lots of ways as one of extremes. It went from periods of intense love and connection to my mother, to long periods of absolute fear and anxiety in her absence. There was always an intense fear that she was going to leave us, so much so, as a small child, I did everything possible to keep the peace between my brother and sister, who seemed oblivious to what I considered the threat to her mental fragility. In lots of ways, I find as an adult, it is a challenge for me to be truly honest in expressing my feelings to others. The old anxiety pattern kicks in and I kind of lose connection with what is best for me, so I come across indecisive and overly appeasing, but it is something I am working on.

At times, mum's state of mind was delicate, and it took something rather insignificant to lead to a cascade of events. I remember being about four. She had been up in Dublin visiting her mother, who was a difficult emotionally-manipulative character. In her distraction, trying to rush here and there at her mother's beck and call, she clipped a wing mirror on her car. This resulted in a disproportionate emotional tsunami once she got home. I just remember her being distraught. Memory and time are poor bed fellows, so I am unsure if this event resulted in an event that will stay with me all my life. My sister, brother and myself are in a room in the house, knowing something awful is happening in the house. Mum has taken an overdose and our neighbour and her daughter, who was a doctor, are there, probably trying to make her vomit. This was the only attempt I remember, but seemingly there were others.

I don't want to paint an inaccurate picture. The above events were only probably a small chunk of our lives. My overall impression of my childhood was that of an amazing one, full of love, freedom, and adventure. I loved the independence that growing up on the farm gave me. I felt safe to head off and explore on my own. On these occasions I did not worry about Mum. I was immersed in nature; I could breathe, run, and jump, get lost in an idyllic world with no responsibilities or concerns. I am aware I have a strong tendency towards escape and escaping, hence I find it difficult to settle in jobs, places etc. when it gets stressful, but I am aware of this now, so that in itself weakens these tendencies. I read something interesting recently, that says that children who experience an absence of a primary caregiver have physiologically less cortisol receptors, therefore cortisol floods their system more easily. They have a lower stress threshold.

As a child I was fascinated by religion and remember sitting in our local church, convinced that I had heard someone, who I assumed to be Big Lad upstairs, call my name. I obviously thought I was meant for better things and a bit special, a bit of an ego for a nine-year-old. I remember kneeling in front of a statue in my parents' room for hours, and I loved pretending I was St. Patrick, with a cloak and staff. I was also pretty taken by nuns, particularly ones in the closed orders. We went to St. Bernadette's final resting place in France (Nevers) and it left a great impression on me. I wanted to become a priest and went to the local parish priest and said as much, to which he suggested I come back to him when I was a bit older. I am no longer religious, but I am drawn to Buddhist philosophy, or any philosophy which promotes seeing the beauty in each other and bringing love to the parts of ourselves and each other, which we usually criticise. I would say I am agnostic. I simply don't know, but would love to believe that there is life beyond this earthly one. Of course, there must also be other planetary life in the universe, but it would be reassuring to know that there is life, after death, that we exist in some form, somewhere, and that we remain connected to those we love. After my mother decided to part this life on her own terms, in my distress in the months following her suicide, I went to mediums. These experiences mostly left me feeling enraged and vacuous as many were obviously charlatans, playing on vulnerabilities of those in crisis. I did have one powerful experience which was spine-tinglingly spooky. It gave me hope that indeed there was more to this existence than our short time on this pale blue dot. I have also had dreams in which I really believe my mum has come to me and they were beautiful, nothing that could be conjured up by my brain, but something bigger than anything of this earthy realm.

Trips to the west to visit our dad's family were also very exciting. I remember one particular occasion when we visited my father's sister, my Aunty Ann, her husband, Uncle Paul and our cousins, in the beautiful, tranquil part of the rural Irish midlands where they lived. They had a dairy farm and all you could hear outside, in the gentle summer evening light, was the bellowing of the cows at milking time. How I loved these visits, the smells of the farmyard and the fields of hay bails. Miles of sky above and miles of unchartered nature all around. Every detail magnified in my child's eye. A vegetable patch, through which a crooked, uneven path made its way down steps to the dung-strewn lane, across from which was the milking parlour and the yard. The bellowing of cattle, the smells, the light and shadow of evening, the peace, innocence and fresh knowing of childhood. Back in the kitchen, we would, all of us, sit in the corner of the room, the aga throwing out waves of warmth and comfort. My Aunty Ann setting the table for the tea (it was always an egg salad!). My Uncle Paul making us laugh as he let his dentures drop, his lovely smiling eyes. How I loved listening to himself and Aunty Ann, just sensing the bond of friendship and love between them. In later years, I saw them dance together. How elegantly they moved in-step, a love I could only dream of. They were (and are) such lovely, grounded people and visits to their house would inevitably end up in interesting and entertaining stories and laughter around the tea table. Best of all, I remember my lovely mother sat in the corner, sitting there, gangly knees crossed awkwardly, a *More* cigarette in hand, telling stories. Unable to tell a joke properly, in these moments she was possibly at her funniest. She was, as we say in Ireland, 'gas' and unwittingly so. Back then sitting in that cosy kitchen in rural Westmeath, so many years ago now, in my eyes at least, she took centre stage and brought light and warmth into our world. As we sat in these beautiful moments of shared experience, my father would tell tall tales and I would ask him again and again to tell us stories and jokes that we as a family had all heard a thousand times. With perfect delivery and wit, he had the accents of his characters off to a tee. In these moments, my lovely parents would unwittingly hold court. My Uncle Paul's unmistakable laugh, my lovely Aunty Ann, gentle and kind, enjoying it all. In those precious moments, my mother's sadness disappeared, and her true nature revealed itself in all its beauty. When we were surrounded by our extended family, it felt like nothing could touch us. Nothing horrible existed in those moments. None of the troubles in 'the North', no thoughts of the alienation of interminable school days, no sibling warfare, none of the fear of an imminent hospitalisation, just safety, laughter and love.

This is what brings me home. These are the balanced truths of existence. We can lose perspective so easily and paint the saddest of pictures, but when we open our hearts, we find ourselves in a lofty gallery, its walls mounted with paintings depicting the beautiful, tender and heart-touched moments of our lives. We revisit not only the difficult times, but we also remember experiences of kindness and love. Our lives are a rich tapestry, one with threads of gold amongst the jute.

Interlude 1.1: The Sea Woman

They came and they came again
She fought them back with strength and strain
Alone she stood on the storm-beaten shore
Waiting for the skies to open no more
But years upon years, it steadily rose, dark clouds of pain
and oceans of cold
Seeing their rage, her footing she steadied, with love in her
heart and song in her belly

This solitary woman 'came known in the land
Her strength and her love, one man did command
In each other's heart they grew and did blossom and
Children of love, she brought forth to her bosom
From howling winds and wild skies of rain
She covered their ears, to protect them from pain

And still the storm brewed its rage
Yet she danced on its shores
Ever holding its gaze

As time did unfold, she still fought and persisted
With the love of a man, the sea's call she resisted

Glimpses of sunlight fell on her soul
Her ankles she turned hard rock into snow

When she'd done all her dancing, farewells and enchanting
Her children, she set down at her feet
She reached out her palm, bade adieu to the land
And her spirit she gave to the oceans

The Long Way Round

GETTING OFF THE bus on Nassau Street, I threw my rucksack over my shoulder, took a deep breath and followed the old stone wall towards College Green. The street was teeming with people; office workers, tourists, and happy-go-lucky students returning to start a new academic year. It was October 1995 and as I passed through the front arch of Trinity College Dublin for the very first time, I felt a heady mixture of excitement and nervousness, my stomach in knots. Heading into the registration hall, I met a girl who would go onto to be one of my closest friends during my time at university and into adulthood. I still have the student card which I was given that first day. I look like a right country bumpkin with a big wide smile, a spotty complexion, unsophisticated clothes and a pseudo-Bouffant haircut. I do, however, look as happy as the proverbial Larry, staring out of the photograph into my future. Now, four years later, I stood once again in Front Square, which buzzed excitedly with students all bedecked in their graduation finery. I remember it being a glorious day, the sun beaming down on us and a vast, blue-sky above us. The intervening years had forged unshakable friendships, as we helped each other through the challenges and fun of university life. To also share this day with my parents was for me, of the utmost importance acknowledging that their sacrifices, concern and encouragement had finally paid off.

My father in his trusty navy suit and my mother elegantly turned out as ever in her new 'rigout' with matching hat. They both radiated happiness. Finally, their youngest had made it through the educational system, after what seemed a painful and protracted delivery through the scholastic birth canal.

It had been a long road alright. Never one to take the straightforward route, I had given my poor parents plenty of sleepless nights, as I rode my own self-engineered rollercoaster of mistakes and learning over the years. From a very young age, I recall clearly the frustration and embarrassment I felt in terms of my inability to grasp things intellectually. I had only just turned four years of age when I excitedly headed into *big* school, for my first day with my oversized bag and Muppets lunchbox. Realising that my mother was in fact *not* going to be sitting right beside me in junior infants came as a bit of a shock, to say the least. Perhaps, a year later, having come to terms with the school routine, I clearly remember sitting at the kitchen table one day with my very patient father. There we sat with a heap of coins in front of us, him placing a one penny piece on top of a two pence piece, asking me what this would give me. *A packet of jelly babies?* I may have thought to my five-year-old self. Instead, I suspect there was a good deal of silence, me slowly and clumsily counting on my stubby fingers, my legs dangling mid-air, moving backwards and forwards in slowly increasing increments, as my silent despondency took shape. I do not use this word likely. It seems odd to say now, but there it was, a five-year-old, despairing at his inability to solve sums. I saw every such challenge as a test of my self-worth. I always looked up to my big sister who was brilliant at maths and also happened to be a pretty cool cucumber into the bargain. Did I attribute intellectual ability to emotional stability? Certainly, I saw in her the steady rock to which I could cling during the odd emotional maelstrom at home.

Whatever it was, faced with a question requiring my consideration, a cognitive fog would descend. I had the feeling that there was some obstacle in my way, around which I could not see, and to step forward could result in tripping over a dodgy precipice and falling to a premature, ugly and painful demise. I definitely needed to get out more!

I think it is fair to say that most of us have memories from our young school days, that will be forever imprinted on our psyche, like roughly etched graffiti on a school desk which reads 'sex'. It was a lovely sunny day and I remember distinctly standing there in the classroom during the school break with the teacher, while all the other children played outside. Even the fact that I was indoors with 'teacher' when everyone else was outside, weighed upon me. The muffled sounds of their fun and freedom contrasted with the dread I felt in the pit of my stomach. A man facing the firing squad would have felt more upbeat. A clearly unhappy and dour looking Miss McDonald pointed up to the clock and asked me the time. *Where is the big hand? Where is the little one?* I couldn't think straight for the mounting panic within. In fairness, I had plenty of time to work this out, by virtue of the fact that her face, hardened in agitation at my stupidity, could literally have stopped a clock. Miss McDonald was probably only in her mid-20s, and I can still see to this day her obvious exasperation with this dim-witted boy.

As a child, my skill set lay in facial recognition and analysing moods. I could identify a mood of a significant adult at 30 paces. I could sniff it out. Hyper vigilance was my middle name; a state which I now recognise triggered my little amygdala, that tiny part of our midbrain which sends us free-falling into clouds of anxiety, disarray and confusion. Needless to say, poor Miss McDonald wasted her tea break, and I was certainly none the wiser when it came to the auld clock business.

Being sent to the 'remedial' class in primary school was not exactly the confidence-builder I needed. In the company of my fellow intellectual misfits, I cannot recall learning anything whatsoever. A highlight of those early primary school years was being given the job of bringing around not-so-hot cross buns and cartons of milk to the less privileged in our class. This was pure heaven to me, as on the one hand I got to leave 'hell', also known as *an seomra ranga* (the Irish for classroom) and secondly, I am sure I used to devour the odd bun when no one was looking.

Things started to improve when I went into first class with the lovely Miss Rabbitte, an incredibly kind-hearted woman with a gentle, encouraging and inspiring spirit. I can still remember listening to the lovely way she used to read us a story. You could hear a pin drop. We hung, wide-eyed, on her every word. Academically, she put no pressure on me, but hoped by osmosis, something might sink in. Sadly, this was not to be but, without doubt, I became a happier, less anxious child. So, when it came to the end of the school year and she asked me if I would 'stay back' with her for another year, my joy knew no bounds. That evening I went home thrilled with myself and excitedly told my parents that Miss Rabbitte wanted me to stay back with her.

One act of kindness by Miss Rabbitte improved things immeasurably and by the time I was ready to go to secondary school, I was more confident, more sociable and academically stronger. I certainly enjoyed my secondary school years to a large extent, which I would attribute to a combination of making two or three very close friends, that I have to this day, and developing a keen interest in various subjects. I remember particularly falling in love with English literature and would have happily written essay-type answers on *Wuthering Heights*, Shakespeare's *King Lear* and poetry 'til the cows came home.

PE (Physical Education), on the other hand, was never my strong point and I would avoid it at all costs. The only goal I ever scored in football was an own goal. I remember the moment clearly. Realising I had managed to kick the ball somewhere between the goal posts (with my eyes closed), I was absolutely elated for one single millisecond, only for it to dawn on me in the ensuing moments, probably due to a few dirty looks and sighs of annoyance, I had volleyed the ball past our *own* goalkeeper. Usually, when it came to picking teams, it was either me or the most rotund of pupils who were the last to be reluctantly picked from the bottom of the barrel. Don't get me wrong, I would have been very grateful if they had just said outright 'Listen, we don't want you on our team,' because the feeling was entirely mutual. I would have preferred to squirrel away a couple of hours in the school library or even endure a double maths lesson just to avoid the football field. It did not help that I fancied the PE teacher, who seemed oblivious to my existence. I recall being absolutely stunned when my year report arrived in the post at home and under 'PE', the fine figure of a Cork man had written 'Excellent student'. *Excuse me? Do you mean excellent at inventing all sorts of reasons to miss PE? 'Sir, I forgot my gear.', 'Sir, I took my sister's gymslip by accident.', 'Sir, salivating at your toned and beautiful body, I accidentally tripped over my own drool and smashed my knee. Can you rub it better please?'* Any old excuse and he seemed happy enough to let me off. I must admit my mother was a wonderful ally in terms of writing the occasional 'sick note'. She herself a bit of sports reject in school, had a similar dislike for all things PE-related so, knowing my 'unique' sporting prowess, she happily squiggled a quick note for me of a Wednesday morning. Luckily in our last year, due to the more pressing concern of the Irish Leaving Certificate Examinations, there was absolutely no pressure in terms of the old PE.

Not having a clue what university course to apply for, I put my name down for a degree in Bachelor of Commerce and French, simply because it sounded good, my best friend had applied for the same course (but in Dublin), but most importantly because the course was in Edinburgh. Always the romantic, I thought on leaving my beloved but homophobic Ireland, I would meet the man of my dreams in some far-flung foreign land and frankly Scotland sounded perfect. There was the accent for a start, and I heard Edinburgh was a historic and beautiful city. Lo and behold, it was indeed, and my first year got off to a great start.

My mother and father brought me over on the boat. Arriving at the halls of residence, I would say I looked the part with my hippy clothes, leather jacket, Kurt Cobain-type haircut and attitude. I had just turned 18 and probably showed little emotion when saying goodbye, but I know deep down I was heart-broken and scared stiff. This fear soon abated however, when I made some great friends on my corridor. My next-door neighbour was a tall and kind-hearted Finnish chap called Ville. I secretly fancied him (acne and all) but knew he was off bounds as he had hooked up with a half-Canadian, half-Finnish girl just days into Freshers' Week. Still and all, I would happily sit in his room and watch him effortlessly play his guitar, his long talented fingers gliding up and down the fret board. Oh, to be that fret board! I also loved our deep chats that would often run late into the night, interrupted frequently by his girlfriend. How inconsiderate of her! Truth be told, I had ambivalent feelings about the aforementioned Suli. On a one-to-one, she was a lovely girl, but when she was in a crowd, she devoured attention and stuck like a limpet to my Finnish friend.

Over the course of a few months, I made other good friends and secretly liked being called 'Father', due to my Irish accent and the popularity of the sitcom *Father Ted* at the time. The nights out were fantastic as well. Heading out to clubs that played grunge music was my idea of heaven. Music was, and still is, of extreme importance in my life. With not a penny to my name or an iota of pecuniary sense, I took out a £400 overdraft and bought a 'mahussive' stereo, on which I played every grunge anthem known to man. Needless to say, within a few months I had to sell my beloved stereo and my collection of rare CDs.

I also found myself a job as an office cleaner in downtown Edinburgh. Cleaning the offices was a satisfying experience as I had the place to myself. Toilet cleaning, on the other hand, was not my favourite task of an evening but still in all, a little bit of hard work after a day of missing lectures and living on Alpen, was an education in itself.

Most of my friends settled in quite well academically, but as the year went on, I went to fewer and fewer lectures, having realised within weeks of landing in the Edinburgh, that Business Studies bored me to tears. So, instead of going to lectures I spent most my time playing guitar, smoking joints and wandering the streets of Edinburgh. My jovial Fr. Dougal persona concealed a darker and sadder facet of my personality. My expeditions to the city centre took on an obsessive nature, in my heart-aching desire to meet a loving man who might pull me out of the spiralling pit into which I was falling. These daily jaunts brought me to all sorts of unsavoury places; ones which I know now caused untold damage to my crumbling self-worth. This went on for several months until eventually my financial worries, academic apathy and psychological distress prompted a phone call home to argue my case for deliverance. My lovely parents did not give in straightaway, hoping things might work out. But within a few phone calls, they soon realised that a little time at home and a fresh start might just be answer.

So it was, after a great summer at home with my beloved friends and a few pound in my pocket from my summer job in a local restaurant, I found myself heading up on the bus to Dublin in early October 1995 to start a science degree with which I would eventually fall in love. Having covered a wide range of subjects in the first two years, I then specialised in physiology in the final two years. From start to finish I found Physiology fascinating. Like a beacon illuminating the darkness, I was transported into the complex universes of the human body. Terms such as 'signal transduction' were a sultry temptress to my corruptible grey matter. An 'excitatory post synaptic potential' was enough to send me around the twist altogether. Don't even get me started on the chemical cascades at cellular membranes, modifying protein channels etc. etc. I think I need to lie down now. Upregulation. Downregulation. All of these phenomena driving the very mechanics of human existence. *Am I alone in my fascination?*

I won't explain the minutia of my final year project, but it was a love affair like no other. I was especially fortunate as my supervisor, one of our lecturers Professor Marina Lynch, was an incredible teacher. She conveyed complex physiology in simple, straight-forward language. She taught me so much more than just neuroscience, including how to communicate, in plain and simple language, the nuts, bolts and beauty of everything that makes our physiology the remarkable symphony that it is.

So, having closed the final chapter of our physiology texts and descended the old wooden stairs of our department, with its smell of laboratory mice, here we sat on our graduation day in a wood-panelled room with an ornate ceiling with portraits of aloof academics scowling down at us from on high.

Sitting towards the front of the large hall, we students sat next to each other like giddy nine-year-olds, while our families were directed to benches toward the rear. The initial excitement waned, as it was clear within a few minutes that the entire duration of the ceremony for over three hundred students would proceed in Latin. Now, I did study Latin for three years in secondary school and I don't think I was too bad, but ask me to explain one word of what was said, and I draw a blank. *Pilus Crapus Magnus* is how I would sum up the proceedings. An hour into it, beginning to lose the will to go on, we perked up when we recognised names from our own physiology cohort. Up until this point in the ceremony, there was polite clapping from those congregated, as each candidate was called to the front to collect their degree. Shifting nervously in my seat, aware for the first time that students were called on an alphabetical basis, I then heard my name called out and went to stand. From the back of the room, I heard my mother yelp in delight and clap like billio! (My sister tells me my mother also leapt out of her seat.) Slight embarrassment gave way to exceeding pride as I went to collect my first-class honours degree, sensing the warmth, love and humanity that my beautiful mother brought to the proceedings. I think I may be correct in saying I even saw one of the cadaver-like professors crack a smile, relieved that his tedious task was momentarily interrupted.

It is an understatement to say that my graduation day was one of the most memorable of my life thus far. For me, it was a monumental and significant turning point in my life. Backed by the love and support of my family, friends and educators and my own hard work, I realised finally that all the years of self-criticism and self-doubt had not defeated me.

If I could return to that classroom in 1979, I might stand beside that little boy looking up at the clock, put my arm around him and say, 'Don't worry, it will come together. You're a great boy. Don't mind moody Miss McDonald.' He'd laugh and we would walk hand in hand out the door to the joy and laughter of a child's playground.

Mum & me on the big day, June 1999

Interlude 1.2: Nuclear Fallout

An unmade fire, an ugly thing.
A silent room that she would have filled.
He walks from empty room to empty room.
Checks the weather.
'Do the clothes need to be taken in?'

Looking out the window
My heart folds, collapses
Sitting in his car studying a town map.
The emptiness of hours.

What of the map of his heart?
Where would it lead him?
To a distant grave where she lies now.

The fire in the sitting room of his soul, dead, decayed, dust

What I would give for her to enfold him in her arms again.
To soothe the silent boy within, who bleeds, slowly.

Better Late than Never

WE ALWAYS TEND to remember with clarity, those very significant moments in our lives, when a situation or person, perhaps unwittingly, changes us fundamentally and forever. The image that comes to my mind is one of those old naval ships from centuries past, which on account of some decision or other made by the captain, changes its course. Often, it's the case that we ourselves may not be at the helm, but another redirects our course. Be it an act of kindness or an act of cruelty, obvious or subtle, we may be unaware at the time that this moment will be forever etched into our memory for as long as we are living and breathing. Somehow our brains can compartmentalise these powerful moments in memory. Perhaps the conditions were just right; the right quantities of vulnerability, uncertainty, receptivity and an unconscious need to go beyond our level of understanding up until that point in our lives. I remember one such moment on an otherwise unremarkable day, in a tiny kitchen in Belfast, Norther Ireland. It was 1996. I was 21, nearing the end of my time at university. It felt to me that a new world order was emerging. I was living in a peaceful city, which up until a few months previous, had been a war zone. I remember playing over and over again, The Cranberries' track Dreams which had topped the charts a few years previous. There was something in the energy of that song that spoke of a new Ireland, a new world to step out into. As exciting as all this was, something deeply unsettled within me could not celebrate this enlightened time. I was just a few months into my first ever adult relationship. Prior to meeting my first boyfriend, who was from Belfast, I had never even kissed, (or at least properly) let alone gone out with anyone.

Not strictly true. Permit me to digress briefly. Back in my teens, there was a good deal of pressure on teenagers all over Ireland to go to what is called the 'Gaeltacht', an Irish language college. Sent off from Dublin on the train, we spent three precious weeks of our summer holidays in the most rural and conservatively Catholic outposts on the island. Nationalist training camps in all but name, one evening ritual involved attending the *céilí*. This was a traditional dance where girls stood on one side of the room and the boys on the other. On alternate nights, the boys chose a girl and then danced with her to traditional Irish jigs and reels, overseen by nationalist, politically biased *múinteoirí* (teachers), in an effort to immerse our impressionable young minds in all things Irish. That moment of crossing the dance floor to ask a girl was almost as painful as my PE lessons in school. Beetroot-red with self-consciousness, you made your way up to the top of the queue to run and vault over the wooden horse, or not as the case may be (I'm sure it wasn't just me who never made it over the bloody horse?). Anyway, two and bit weeks into this *céilí* business, everyone it seemed had a girlfriend. I had not and was painfully aware of this fact and obviously worried what others might think of me, as teenagers and non-teenagers are not averse to doing. I had noticed one particular girl, who was into The Cure and wore a long, blue, woolly jumper. I thought she was pretty cool, so if I was going to get myself off the hook somehow, she was the girl. I went up to her, asked her to dance and then proceeded to ask her if she wanted to go out with me. What possessed her to say yes to this spotty, ginger guy with pseudo-Bouffant hairstyle and seriously uncool clothes is beyond me. Needless to say, she obviously had horrendous eyesight or was as desperate as me not to stand out from the crowd yet again. I remember rising panic and regret within seconds of my suggestion, knowing deep down I was insincere in my intentions. My conscience, soaked in good old Catholic Irish guilt, pricked me to the core and by the end of the dance I confessed that it wasn't going to work, so I unduly dumped her (as gently as I could) before I had even given heterosexuality a shot. I knew even back then as a spotty teenager, I was different from most of my peers.

Fast-forward eight years of repressed sexuality, here I stood in a kitchen with my boyfriend's (gay) landlord. It was the summer holidays and I had ventured up from Dublin to spend the three months living and working in Belfast. When I look back on my then new landlord, David, I realise what an incredibly kind man he was. Only in his mid to late 30s at the time, he seemed to me years beyond that in terms of his experience, knowledge, wit and wisdom. Not to sound too melodramatic, the thing was, in terms of the skills required to enjoy an adult relationship, I was frozen in time at that *céilí* in rural west of Ireland. Within weeks of meeting my new boyfriend, far from being in ecstasy and feeling secure, I was reeling in inadequacy and insecurity, looking at him and his friends, who I perceived to be 'real' gay people with experience and composure, unlike me, who felt like a complete teenage fish out of water (do fish get to their teens?? I don't think so!). Even the mere mention of his former exploits was enough to send me into a spin, persecuting myself and him. The poor chap. My new landlord, sensitively aware of this mess of agitation and insecurity in front of him, handed me a small postcard and told me to study it. It depicted twelve little caricatures of gay people in tiny individual frames. There was handle-bar moustached guy, black guy, fat guy, leather guy, a bear (not of the pawed variety), an effeminate and extremely thin guy, a pretty 'normal' looking guy, a guy in uniform, and so the list continued. This simple little depiction of diversity was about all my poor little frazzled brain could cope with in that moment, but it stuck. It landed, at least consciously. At a deeper emotional level, I would wonder has it yet really landed. Almost 25 years and a couple of relationships later, I would struggle to align myself with any of these caricatures, not that anyone should aspire to align themselves to a particular 'type' but, more importantly, I realise that, in spite of the opportunities out there to embrace my sexuality, it is only in the last few years that I have begun to enjoy my sexuality and start to accept myself as I am.

I have matured and relaxed a good deal, and that has been reflected in largely being more at ease in my relationships. The last two for eight and seven years respectively, so in gay (dog) years, what's that? 47 and 51 years. Good going!!! Still and all, if I am honest enough about it, describing myself as gay, feels odd even now. Something foreign to my sense of self. Of course, we are so much more than just our gender or sexuality, but nonetheless they are critically important aspects that to deny can only be an obstacle to being fully alive. Admittedly, I love the male form and I have known beautiful intimacy with men, when not succumbing to the 'norms' that have been created around sex and sexuality. Lastly, it is most definitely with a man that I imagine myself making a deep and intimate connection in the future, in terms of a life-long partnership.

These ideals do not come easily, however, and require an element of work on my part in terms of dismantling the misconceptions I have around sexuality. In an effort to clear the cobwebs from the 'auld' subconscious, I was fortunate enough to find an extremely skilled and compassionate psychotherapist about three years ago. This was without doubt one of the best things I have ever done. How the poor woman has put up with my ramblings, I do not know, but amongst the many insights she has inspired, she has helped me to begin to see the 'internalised' homophobia (unconscious, unwanted and unexpressed) I have carried since my earliest years. Put it down to social conditioning, the Catholic Church, or any other obvious target, it really is pointless pointing the finger at this stage of life. Anyway, internalised homophobia is extremely prevalent within the LGBT community. It would explain my historical aversion to the 'camp' stereotype, an inability to not wriggle in my seat at the mere mention of anything related to my sexuality, let alone attend a Gay Pride march (although I think I could handle the latter now no problem, but would sooner walk up a beautiful mountain). Approaching my mid-40s, I am coming to know the simplistic, polarised perceptions

I have had for many years of gay sexuality and perhaps sexuality in general. I ask myself 'Am I still at that flippin' céilí?' I am slowly coming to the point where I realise that the many different and apparently conflicting aspects of sexual / intimate expression are interdependent for a more complete expression of our best self: patience, tenderness, lust, sensitivity, crudeness, vulnerability etc. It feels slightly embarrassing to admit this as a forty-something year old, but hey, better late than never.

A Question of Pride

IN A MONTH in which Pride is celebrated the world over, I sit here aware that pride is not the first word that comes to my mind when thinking about my sexuality. Do I feel pride being gay? If I lack pride in this most fundamental aspect of my identity, if I struggle to truly and fully accept myself as I am, can I honestly say I feel pride, acceptance and love for others, let alone a significant other?

Today a series of events unfolded which answered some of these questions. A good friend contacted me to tell me that he had finally come out to his adolescent teenage sons. The years leading up to this disclosure had been extremely difficult but his need to be honest and open about something so fundamental to his identity, to those he loves most in the world, demanded attention. Emotionally, he was at breaking-point. Coming out to his sons turned out to be a beautiful and emotional experience. He was met by intense love and acceptance from his sons. The relief, he told me, and the overwhelming pride in their reaction, was like a great dam braking. I felt so happy for him that I was on the edge of tears reading his messages. As I went on with my evening, I felt increasingly agitated. I felt my mood sinking and then thoughts surfaced. I realised what was at the root of it was the knowledge that I had never experienced such a catharsis when I 'came out' to my family or friends. The women in my family were strong and loving and showed immediate love and acceptance. With the men, it was a different story. Even opening up to my mum did not break the seal of my emotional yearning. Nothing came unstuck. In fact, something resembling shame and uncertainty remained lodged in my gut, festering. Shortly after my mum got home and told my father, he phoned me and told me that he would accept the news but would not approve. I remember standing in my student flat, holding the receiver to my ear, my heart broken. I felt so adrift, so cut off from anything resembling love. My father has changed his attitude immeasurably in the intervening two decades and is now the most open octogenarian I know. It was just his own social conditioning that took its time to unravel.

Growing up in the 1980s, most of what I had heard about being gay, was spoken of with some degree of detached revulsion. Gay people were considered outcasts, debased, pitiful, modern-day lepers. These were people who died of a horrible disease, like the very talented Freddie Mercury. These were the stereotypes that I, and probably most Irish people thought about when they heard the term gay or lesbian. Even as a child, I loved what Freddie represented. He epitomised an integrity and expression that I did not understand, but I felt deep within. Sadly, TV dished up *Carry On* and *Are you Being Served?* Characters that were the epitome of the camp stereotype. I would squirm uncomfortably in my seat when these characters minced on screen. This was not a sexuality with which I could identify. The effete male, his self-derisory flamboyancy only, in my opinion, encouraged many of us non-stereotypical gay men to lock the doors of our collective closets. They did us a disservice. A modern phenomenon, which I believe is also causing as much damage to our sexual expression is pornography. Unconsciously, we rebuke ourselves for not fitting the image or having the acrobatic prowess of these mechanical sex machines (often good-looking sex machines it has to be said!). Let's wake up, stand up, get real and celebrate who we actually are, what we are and everything we can give of ourselves.

Reeling back the years, I recall my father bitterly mocking a cousin of his who happened to be gay although, in later life, I realised it was not his sexuality that triggered this reaction in my otherwise gentle and loving father. I remember him affecting a limp wrist with vicious vitriol, mimicking the stereotypical behaviour of the time. I remember being shocked to the core that this man, who I loved and respected, could feel that way about gay people. Needless to say, I retreated to the very back of the closet and would have fought my way into Narnia if I could have.

In my early childhood, we lived on a farm in a rural part of county Meath in Ireland, our neighbours living a couple of miles up the road. I recall hiding cut-outs from newspapers with stamp-sized images of people in semi-clad poses. I hid these in what I thought were lofty and cunning hiding places. I recall climbing onto chairs and desks and hiding them amongst my father's paperwork. Not a bad feat for a seven-year-old. What was I thinking? My parents, in fairness to them, most assuredly found these clippings over time, but never said anything. In my very early teenage years, I had one or two friends with whom I messed about with; that is to say we had a bit of a fumble together. I do not recall how exactly these situations arose, but I suppose when you put teenagers with raging hormones in close proximity, the occasional fumble will happen. Choked in confusion and shame, there wasn't a whole lot of talk about it subsequently, but I remember feeling ashamed and dirty. Good old Catholic guilt. It had a knack of insidiously seeping into the psyche of even innocent children.

Edging into the 1990s, in later teenage years, intelligent entertainers and writers like Julian Clary, David

Sedaris and many others, demonstrated through their sharp wit, that they were most defiantly challenging an outdated homophobic society and were most definitely in the driving seat. These were gay men who had an edginess to their humour, a palpable undercurrent of rebellious dissatisfaction with the status quo. This struck a chord with me and gave me hope for a better future. At school I was fortunate not to be bullied, but hearing friends sneakily mimicking one of our other friends, who was somewhat effeminate, was hard to take. Sadly, I wasn't brave enough at the time to stand up for him when these things were being said behind his back. Every slander towards him was one unwittingly aimed at me, but I cannot undo the past now, but I am confident I would not stand for it these days.

I remember lying in bed, when I wasn't 'self-abusing' myself (as the Catholic Church so beautifully put it), frequently imagining the time when I would meet the man of my dreams, with whom I would fall in love. Despite all the toxic rhetoric and reverberations of societal homophobia of youth, I knew even then, aged 13, that nothing, absolutely nothing could possibly be wrong with something so beautiful as love. No vitriolic gesture or word, no religious diatribe nor comedic self-effacement could contaminate something so pure, so natural as mutually consenting adult love, whatever the gender mix. I knew this back then, a self-conscious, spotty, ginger teenager, and I know it now, a gay man in his late 40s with a trendy ginger beard, it must be said (ginger is the new blonde after all!). In spite of this, I still struggle with fully accepting myself. As a very old friend, I once had the privilege to know, said before she died at the age of 102 and after a long full life, 'it's no bed of roses'.

Be that as it may, we are well informed, and now live in a society which encourages expression. It is hard however to unravel the years of conditioning, to literally unravel the neural networks which encode inner criticism like 'you're a faggot'. In spite of this, we can overcome these inner demonic narratives. Like the literary genius Maya Angelou once so cleverly phrased it, 'You may kill me with your hatefulness but still, like dust, I rise'.

It is no strange coincidence that it has taken me until I reached my mid 40s before I found a network of a few lovely, gay male friends. Yes, I met amazing individuals along the way but, for the first time, I now feel part of a tribe. I sense a belonging. Why did it take so long? I can only assume it was my own internal struggles with self-acceptance, my own internalised homophobia. I now happily and proudly call my little tribe, my friends. Men like me who have known what it is to be marginalised, to be outside, looking in but not necessarily wanting to be 'in'. In them, I have found a band of beautiful souls, the purest of hearts, the kindest of men.

Given this is Pride month, and if I was a wee bit braver and wasn't living in a tiny coastal village in Scotland, where everyone knows everyone, I might stand in the village square, clear my throat and shout at the top of my lungs what singer PJ Harvey has bellowed out to searing electric guitars on a Glastonbury stage for years, something that I indeed told myself all those years ago lying in my teenage bed. I might throw my fist to the sky and declare of my sexuality 'This is love, this is love, that I'm feeling, this is love, love, love, that I'm feeling'. It has taken me years to get to this point in my life, the embryonic stages of self-acceptance, perhaps edging slowly and tentatively towards love.

All Packed

PACING THE BEDROOM, occasionally glancing anxiously at my unpacked rucksack lying on the bed and the piles of clothes next to it, I thought to myself *'What the hell am I doing? This is nuts. There are reasons why people don't go to these places.'* Talking myself down from the escalating panic, I told myself I would be grand. *'Whatever happened to those Australians won't happen to me'.* A good friend, who is a GP and has travelled extensively, had told me earlier that same morning, that a group of Australians had been arrested and detained by Iranian authorities only a week prior to my departure and as such I just needed to be that extra bit cautious. She assured me that I would be fine, but just to be aware of what might be deemed risky behaviour. I pictured myself taking photos of dishy Iranian soldiers in front of government buildings, only to be carted off to a cell and ravaged within an inch of my life by a sex starved squaddie. *'I definitely need to bring the camera!'* I thought to myself. As for the Aussies, it turned out that they had camped beside an Iranian military base and flown a drone over the enclosure. I may be a little wet around the ears but, holy God, that is beyond stupidity.

Six months before, when I had booked the itinerary that would take me through Iran, India, Nepal, Myanmar,

Laos, Vietnam and Japan over a five-month period, it had all seemed so exciting. Now that my departure was imminent, my amygdala was in overdrive and anxiety had seeped into the surrounding neuronal landscape. Distracting myself, I devoted my full attention to the packing. *'Okay do I have everything? 17 pairs of underpants, mosquito net, soap dish, supersize sunblock, thermal socks (that could keep a family of Eskimos toasty), six hardback books (including a bible-sized Lonely Planet on Japan), a puncture repair kit...'* Over the following five months I would learn many lessons about life. I would experience incredible human kindness, face cultural norms that would challenge me to my very core and teach me so much about my own intolerance and reactivity, as well as my own patterns of behaviour, but one lesson that will remain with me to my dying day, is to pack minimally. Towards the end of my trip in Japan, I would meet the 'lovely James' (as I secretly named him) and felt like such an idiot when he looked at me in bewilderment at the load that I had carried over thousands of miles. *'A soap dish Martin? Come on. All you need is two pairs of underpants, two t-shirts, one pair of pants, shorts....'* I knew he was right and vowed I would return to Japan and God damn it, I'd be that carefree.

On the afternoon of my departure, I stood at the bus stop with my father waiting for the bus to the airport. The fact that I wouldn't see him, or anyone I knew, for over five months had not really sunk in, which was really a blessing. We gave each other a hug and I climbed on board and waved at him through the window. He looked lonely there on the footpath, but I knew I had to do this for my own growth. It was a journey I needed to make, just something I needed to do for many reasons. Within the hour I was at the airport and in the queue for the flight to Moscow. I had an 18-hour stopover in the Russian capital before flying on to Tehran, and had obtained a transit visa so I could head into the city for my few hours on Russian soil. Standing now in a line of stern looking Russians, I checked in. Just as I was leaving the counter, experiencing a heady mixture of exhilaration and downright terror, the check-in lady called out in a thick Russian accent 'hyu huv lift yur passpurt and burding cart sir' (a little louder and more dismissive than I would have liked, I might add). Feeling like a scolded schoolboy, I smiled, blushed and grabbed them off the counter. 'Oh, Holy Mother of the Divine, you haven't even left the country and you're already making a bags of it!' my inner critic jibed.

At some ungodly hour the next morning we touched down in Sheremetyevo airport, Moscow. On my way towards security I stopped to get my passport out of my bag and headed on, only to realise at the x-ray belt I had left my walking boots down when I had been hunting for my passport. Heading back on myself, I was relieved to see my trusty boots were where I had left them and consciously noted I had three items. Had I needed to wrestle my boots off a hunky Russian guard, I would have put myself through the ordeal. I mean you'd have to, wouldn't you? In my case however, it was far more likely, had I returned five minutes later, a burly six-foot-five cleaner named Inga, with tattoos down her face and a nose ring the size of a satellite dish, might have wrestled me to the ground with her little finger, in my attempt to retrieve my forsaken footwear. Having gotten through security without incident and with all bags accounted for, I headed for the station and took the train to Belorussky Station. Two metro stops later I found myself at Teatralnaya Station, named after the nearby square of the same name, the location of several theatres including the famous Bolshoi Theatre. Adorned with crystal lamps in bronze frames, as well as fluted columns faced with white marble taken from the demolished Cathedral of Christ the Saviour, Teatralnaya Station is a marvel to behold. From here I walked to the Kremlin gardens and was stopped in my tracks by a beautiful sculpture of Emperor Alexander I, who rebuilt the city following the 1812 Napoleonic invasion. Stunning bas-reliefs depicted the victorious and irreverent Napoleon as he made his triumphant way into Moscow.

Famished from the early start, I headed to the nearest café and enjoyed a delicious if unusual breakfast of granola, cottage cheese, blueberries and strawberries washed down with mint tea, all served up by a very friendly young Russian lady. Satiated, I consulted my guidebook and headed in the direction of Red Square. A few minutes later, through an archway in the distance, I felt a burst of childlike excitement as I saw the colourful, ice cream-like domes of St. Basil's Cathedral and almost broke into a sprint with delight. Red Square was more beautiful than I could ever have imagined

and there was a lovely friendly atmosphere about the place.

Dashingly handsome guards stood to attention at various entry points around the square, but it was mostly small groups of tourists that began to trickle into the early morning square. So it was, I spent my one day in the Russian capital visiting exquisitely built palaces and cathedrals, including the Golden Czarina's Palace and the Cathedral of the Assumption. Inside the cathedral were garish but intriguing frescoes depicting the three realms, heaven near the domed ceiling, earth in the middle and towards the bottom the nether world, with its infernal (and let's be honest) more fun-looking naughty goings-on. Deciding to brave the gathering crowds, I joined the queue to view Lenin in his eerie, air-conditioned crypt. Descending into the bowels of the modest building, the temperature dropped several degrees, as did my jaw, when I noticed guards with rifles at the ready, in case one of us idiotic tourists decided to shimmy up to old Vlad for a good old nosey. Lenin's remains are small and shrunken, yet perfectly preserved in that deathly, waxy kind of way. All in all, a one-minute experience, but one which I'm glad I didn't miss. Aware that I would need to get back to the airport in a few hours to catch my connecting flight to Iran, I hopped on the underground and took the Circle line. A friend had suggested, if I was to visit the underground, it was that line I needed to take. Stepping out beneath chandeliers, hanging from superbly decorated ceilings in various stations, I was awestruck by stained glass windows and lofty statues, celebrating Lenin and other Russian patriots.

A few hours later, I sat on the stairs above the busy crowd, waiting to board the plane for Tehran. There was a palpable tension in the air, as many stood in line at the boarding gate, while others huddled in groups around the stairwell. Most of those gathered looked tense and had a serious demeanour. It could have been simply tiredness, but my gut told me otherwise. Were they nervous about returning to their homeland? If so, why? Should I be nervous? What the hell was I doing? Doubt crept over me, like an insidious asp curling its way around dead bark, and visions of being arrested and hurled into an Iranian prison flashed before my eyes. Well, too late now, I thought to myself, as the flight to Tehran was called. No going back now, sunshine. Iranian mothers, lock up your sons. This Irish Ginge is coming to town. Ye ha!

'Ireland, ah, Conor McGregor'

(Tales of a gay ginger in the Islamic Republic of Iran)

I followed an arrow on the wall pointing in the direction of Mecca and thought to myself, *'You're a long way from Tipperary now sunshine.'* I had woken from a very deep, peaceful sleep in a quiet, comfortable room in Tehran's Ibis Airport Hotel, to the faint humming of a plane taking off. Within a few minutes I was suited and booted and had headed downstairs for, what I thought excitedly, would be my first authentic Iranian breakfast. Catering for the Western palate however was a priority for the management at Ibis hotel. Not exactly the spread I had hoped for, it was delicious, nonetheless. A dollop of molasses syrup on my cereal and fruit gave me a much-needed sugar boost, after what had been a late night. I had landed at International Khomeini Airport in Tehran at 2am that day, so after a few hours' sleep and a refreshing shower, an unnatural high was exactly what the Ayatollah had ordered. Only in the country five minutes, I was already admiring the handsome Iranian waiters who crisscrossed the restaurant floor, looking industrious, yet friendly and welcoming. Reminding myself, however, that although being gay is not illegal per se in the country, engaging in a sexual act with someone of the same sex is punishable by imprisonment, corporal retribution, or execution. *'I shall keep my homosexual handies to myself thank you!'* I thought to myself. Irrespective, time for daydreaming was about all that I could afford, as I was on a strict time schedule. I had arranged to meet a man about a SIM. After this I was to make my way speedily to South Terminal Bus station in the capital, to head to my first destination of Kashan. Meeting this Iranian agent (secret or not, I wasn't entirely sure), I had made it a priority to get my hands on a SIM card that would work in the country, in case I ran into difficulty.

Although very advanced in many ways, Iran is an Islamic state under the control of a small, yet powerfully ruthless regime, made up of wealthy clerics and militia. Socially and politically, Iran was an extremely progressive country, forging links with superpowers across the globe, until the Shah (Iran's monarch at the time) was overthrown by the ultraconservative Ayatollah Khomeini, who came to power following the 1979 revolution. The infamous Shia cleric had gained considerable power, by winning support from both the political left and religious conservatives, in the lead up to the revolution. Despite the regime's ruthless oppression of its own people, historically Iran (or Persia as it is also known) is a country which boasts one of the oldest civilisations on earth.

Beginning with the establishment of the Elamite kingdoms in 4000 BC, its imperial power was at its height under Cyrus the Great in the sixth century BC, who ruled the Achaemenid Empire. Its lands stretched from Eastern Europe to the Indus Valley, an area which makes it one of the largest empires in history. In the fourth century BC it fell to Alexander the Great (and ruthless it should be noted) who having lived in the empire's ceremonial capital of Persepolis for seven years, burned it to the ground, leaving only traces of a once progressive and magnificent city. A century later the Persians rebelled and won back their country and its power passed from empire to empire, until the Islamisation of the country by the Arab Muslims in the seventh century AD. More accurately known as the Islamic Republic of Iran, it is the second largest country in the Middle East, with a population of 83 million. Geographically, the country is mountainous and green to the north and desert-like and flat to the south, where it meets the Persian Gulf. It is situated within a geopolitically unstable region, sharing its eastern borders with Afghanistan and Pakistan, while Iraq and Syria lie to its western fringes.

Determined to see as much of this vast country as I could in a mere three weeks, I was on the road to Kashan in no time at all. Three hours south of the capital, Kashan is a busy but modest-sized town in Isfahan Province. Handwoven carpet weaving is synonymous with Kashan, as well as the production of rose water and mint water, specialities in Iran. Isfahan province is also known for its pistachio and saffron growing. Approaching the outskirts of Kashan in our large comfortable bus, I thought I might jump off wherever the two young German women in front of me decided to alight. If ever there was a nationality who had done their homework in terms of research, I was putting my bets on the Germans. I was relieved to get chatting to them when we retrieved our luggage, as in no time at all we were surrounded by friendly but cash-hungry taxi drivers. Everywhere I looked street signs were in Farsi, the national language of Iran. Prior to visiting the country, I had thought in my ignorance that Iranians would speak Arabic. In fact, Farsi belongs to the Indo-European language family, which means it is more closely related to Portuguese than Arabic! Banking these sorts of facts reminds me of my tendency to make broad sweeping assumptions about complex and diverse realities. The truth is that of course there is major diversity culturally, politically, linguistically, and so on between neighbouring peoples and places across the globe. I think this is why travelling to culturally different countries really appeals to me. It challenges my inclination to make gross and inaccurate assumptions. In a sadistic kind of way, I get a dopamine hit when life teaches me how judgemental I can be, even if it is not borne out of malintent, but rather a lack of knowledge.

After a quick lesson from my German friends in how to haggle with smiley but crafty Iranian taxi drivers, the three of us bundled into a small, carpeted taxi. Even the dashboard was carpeted, while tasselled banners hung from the windows. Multiple, large fluffy dice dangled from the rear-view mirror, swinging back and forth in time to an Iranian pop song blaring from the radio. Within minutes, we came to a standstill. It was clear that there was a parade or an event ahead of us. Women and men clad in black filled the streets and loudspeakers threw out a cacophony of discord, which competed with whistling and shouts from the multitude gathered. Later I learned that I had arrived in Iran at the beginning of a two-month religious festival, which remembers a significant Shia martyr and grandson of the Islamic prophet Muhammad. Imam Husayn lived and died in the 7th century AD, coming to an unhappy end, having his head chopped off. Sadly, many of us in the west tend to focus on such grisly goings-on when thinking about regions within the Middle East. Throughout the globe, certainly, there are incredibly corrupt regimes and factions which grab television and newspaper headlines, but we can so easily forget that most people in these countries are peace-loving just like us, wishing to live simple carefree lives. We in the West are often oblivious to how warm, peaceful and kind the majority of Muslims are in this mysterious and beautiful corner of the world. Iran, however, is a sad example of a people living at the mercy of a cruel and corrupt hand where an oppressive and sinister regime perpetrates shocking crimes against its own people.

In Isfahan I stayed with a lovely young woman at a 'homestay' in a leafy suburb of this enchanting city. A feisty, passionate and kind young woman, Bahar had a beautiful lunch ready for me on my arrival and went out of her way to direct my taximan by phone to her guesthouse. She was obviously a well-read and educated young woman with excellent English. Unafraid to speak frankly about the clerical child abuse carried out in her country and the cruelty reigned down upon women in Iran, she explained how not long before, a young woman had been arrested for attending a football game, which is illegal in Iran. Upon being sentenced to two years in prison for the 'crime', she set herself on fire in an act of protest, to bring attention to the injustice experienced by Iranian women. In recent months, the world has been shocked by the brutal retaliation of the Iranian government, in its attempt to suppress nationwide protestors trying to speak out against the regime's brutality. Back in 2019, in a sunlit kitchen in the beautiful city of Isfahan, Bahar explained how she herself had been arrested on four different occasions, simply because her hijab was not hiding enough of her beautiful hair. Standing with her back to me as she washed the dishes, she told me how on one occasion the police broke her leg. She was silent for some time after she made this remark and only when she turned to remove my dishes, did I see she had been crying. This was my first, but not last experience of seeing the sadness in the eyes of these beautiful warm people.

Two days later I found myself hurtling along a dual carriage way with three young German guys in the back of a jeep with Behrooz our guide at the wheel. We were headed for Khara desert. Located 100 kilometres east of Isfahan, this spectacular desert covers 17,000 hectares with the Gavkhouni Wetlands to the east and the Zayandeh-Rood River to the north. Khara is well known in Iran for its beautiful sand dunes, many of which reach over 60 metres in height, the highest in the country, sculpted by the many wind systems that pass through the region. On route we stopped off at Behrooz's family orchard and picked grapes and pomegranates. We then called by a neighbouring fisherman, who pointed into a pool of meandering unfortunates who would satisfy our greedy voracious western appetites. Arriving at Khara just before sunset, I made my way to the top of a sheer, sloping sand dune, and looked across a vast, empty ocean of moving sands. As the sun descended, a beautiful light display played out before my eyes with salmon pink turning to orange, then to a dusty red and finally to a dark mauve. We were told we could go for a wander but to be back for dinner in an hour. Deep down I am a shy creature, so I happily wandered off on my own and soon found a place to sit on top of one of the dunes, away from the three German friends. I closed my eyes and experienced a silence, purer than I had ever known before. You could have heard a solitary scurrying scorpion at a hundred paces. Sitting awhile, I was soon aware of a wind gathering around me, sand grains gently whipping me. Opening my eyes, I saw the stars peeping through the dark desert canopy.

After a half hour or so, I made my way back down in the darkness towards the fire that Behrooz had made at our campsite. Alone with him and our cook Mohammed, who was preparing our evening meal, I was offered a locally distilled spirit called Arak. Allah above, but this type of Iranian moonshine puts our native Irish *poitín* to shame. Just as potent at a heady 60% alcohol, its main ingredients include dates and raisins and renders its consumer a fire-breathing zombie, well momentarily at least. Due to Islamic intolerance of alcoholic beverages, Arak is illicitly produced and is in effect Persian vodka. When the sun dips below the desert horizon and temperatures can plummet to near freezing, old Arak is exactly the kind of friend you would want close by. Behrooz our guide had a beautiful, smiling face and an easy laugh, so typical of Iranian hospitality. While we waited for our German friends, we sat in the camp light, and he gave me the lowdown on various Persian musical instruments. I explained to him that earlier that year I had visited Norway with my father and one Sunday morning we had visited a Lutheran cathedral. Looking around the magnificent building, it was obvious preparations were being made for the service. Out of nowhere the most beautiful music filled the cathedral, soaring heavenward. I was stuck to the spot, and I could feel each note touch something deep within my soul, like a gentle sun shower on dry and cracked soil. After it had finished, I went up to the musician and thanked him. Asking where he was from, he told me he was Iranian and the instrument he had played was a santoor, a hammered dulcimer of Persian origins. We know from Assyrian and Babylonian stone carvings that it was played as far back as 669 B.C. Originally made from tree bark and stones, and strung with goat intestines, the santoor is considered by musical authorities to be the mother of the harp, the Chinese yangqin, the harpsichord and the hammered dulcimer. It is an instrument that calls to your heart and leaves you spellbound, reminding you of all that is beautiful in life.

So it was that we sat at our campfire, sipping Arak, listening to the crackling of dry twigs on the fire. The German friends returned for their dinner. The beautiful stillness was somewhat disrupted by their return, as there was a short-lived but heated discussion between two of the friends about some political issue. The awkward atmosphere soon dissipated as we sat staring into the campfire with the aroma of baked trout, which was soon served up with fried potatoes, mushrooms and fresh tomatoes. Under a star-studded sky, we ate the delicious meal and not long afterwards a guitar (sadly not a santoor) was strummed, and our spirits were soothed. A couple of hours later, during which I had cracked an Irish joke or two which went down like The Hindenburg, we all trundled off to our sleeping bags and tents. Determined to make the most of my time in the desert, I asked Behrooz if it would be safe if I wandered to the top of one of the sand dunes and slept up there in my sleeping bag under the stars. He beamed at me and told me to fire ahead. Like an excited child, I grabbed my sleeping bag and climbed the steep bank of a nearby sand dune. I unfolded my sleeping bag and climbed in, having of course brushed my teeth and put in my curlers beforehand (honestly reader, I kid you not. If you are going to be dessert for a passing rattler, you may as well go out in style!) I slept well that night and woke to a beautiful sunrise.

Behrooz and a couple of the others climbed up to where I had slept and admired the rising sun. Animal footprints in the sand around my sleeping bag were soon pointed out and I realised I wasn't as stylish or tasty as I had thought myself to be and some wild dog or other decided to sniff out a more appetising meal during the night. Thanks be to Allah! On our way out of the desert, Behrooz drove us to a nearby salt flat. These are dried-up desert lakes which, prior to evaporation, were rich in salts and minerals. Formed in closed desert hollows however, the water has nowhere to escape and due to the intense desert heat, it evaporates faster than it can be replenished. Salts and minerals are therefore left behind as a solid layer. In the intense dry heat, salt flats are typically a brilliant white under the hot, desert sun. It felt to me as if I were standing on a vast and brilliant white ocean, made up of infinite hexagonal shapes. These are created by the repeated freezing and thawing processes of water, which create natural convection pattern.

Leaving behind the beauty of the Khara desert, we made on our way back to Isfahan. Sitting in the front with Behrooz, I asked him for his opinion on the government regime in Iran. Without a hint of bitterness, but infused with sorrow, he spoke softly of how his people live under a ruthless and economically driven regime, presented to the world in the guise of religion. A tiny minority of cruel and divisive religious clerics and militia repress their own people in both brutal and insidious ways. A single party state, those who disagree with the regime (who in my experience were most people I spoke to) and are openly resistant to it, have been known to disappear, to be tortured or even murdered. He spoke of his many friends who had left Iran, their beloved country so rich in history, culture and decency, to live a life of freedom, but never again to return to their homeland. A silence filled the gap between us, and I saw tears in his eyes, as he stared ahead on a highway in an Iranian desert under a vast, blue sky.

On my last night in Isfahan, despite my protests, Bahar and Behrooz insisted on treating me to a lovely supper in a beautiful hotel courtyard in the old city. The hotel was once a caravanserai, a roadside inn, where weary travellers and tradespeople could rest with their camels when walking the busy trading routes of the region. The most famous of these routes, the Silk Road was effectively re-routed in the 16th Century to pass through Isfahan by the Persian King, Shah Abbas I (1588-1629), so the capital city would enjoy a trading monopoly within the great empire. So here we sat on a balmy evening, under a star-lit sky, surrounded by beautiful gardens with intricately decorated fountains cooling the courtyard, living the life of Persian royalty. We ate Aush, a delicious Persian noodle soup made from herbs, pulses, spinach and sour cream, covered with caramelised onions. For dessert, I was to sample Faloodeh, semi-frozen vermicelli noodles bathed in rosewater syrup, served with lime juice. There are simply no words to describe this delicacy. As tasty as the food was and as stunning as the surroundings were, what impressed me most of all was the generosity of these two Iranian friends. Neither was affluent in any way, quite the contrary, but both were incredibly warm and thoughtful, wanting only to welcome this ginger Irishman to their magnificent country.

The following day I took a bus 200 miles southwest to the desert city of Yazd. Having found my accommodation for the night, I went on the hunt for some grub. Wandering into a little grocery store to enquire if there was a nice little café nearby, a young chap standing at the counter offered to take me on the back of his motorbike to his friend's restaurant, as they offered a good Iranian lunch there. Being the naïve eejit that I am, I jumped on the back of his motorbike, and headed for Allah knows where. Finally, he stopped down a back alley, switched off the ignition and invited me to come with him. (Danger is my middle name, dear reader). Knocking on a door, I was soon beckoned into a vast restaurant by a very smiley young man. As the only customer in the place, I was brought to a nearby table, beside which was a carpeted divan of sorts, upon which I was invited to recline my Irish posterior. After a quick look at the menu (all in Farsi), I just pointed to one with a nice picture. For all I knew, it could have been Roasted Roland Rat but who was I to argue.

Having been given a glass of refreshing rosewater, the young waiter asked, 'you are from what country?' I delivered what I thought sounded like a reasonably intelligible answer, but alas I may as well have been speaking Swahili. Arduous attempts were made to decipher exactly this strange-sounding far-off land, in my obviously incomprehensible accent.

'Vineland?', 'island?', 'Germany?' (Exsqueeze me??) so with my best BBC accent, and after some time it has to be said, my motherland's identity eventually resulted in a chemical cascade of understanding and enlightenment in a teensy-weensy synaptic cleft somewhere deep and distant in this incredibly friendly, young Iranian's cerebrum. 'Ah Ireland......Conor McGregor', he exclaimed excitedly. Not for the first time since I had arrived in this beautiful country, I stifled a silent scream and secretly sought forgiveness from Joyce, Yeats, Wilde and their ilk. 'Yes indeed, the very country' I said, smiling, pushing down a deepening sense of betrayal. I could have attempted to enlighten him as to the many celebrated creative minds which have come from that land of saints and scholars, that distant Western European outcrop, but I let it go. Giving him the old 'one-two', I beamed at him and feigned pride in aforementioned Mr. McGregor. Having brought me a delicious mystery lunch from the kitchen, he proceeded to take out his iPhone and show me, in order of priority, photos of his dog, an ugly Rottweiler called Donald, his motorbike, his girlfriend, and his extended family. Not for the first time, my number was requested as he was keen to keep in touch (and work on his English) with this strange looking foreigner.

Sharing a little of our respective histories and political set-ups, the conversation frequently lost its way in a tangle of linguistic confusion. Blank expressions abounded between himself and myself, his English six million times better than the paltry few words of Farsi I possessed. Google Translate can come in very handy in such situations, so here we stood, me trying to explain that Irish was Ireland's national tongue, he, giving me a concise five-minute breakdown of Iranian history and culture over the last 2000 years, Google Translate negotiating the linguistic landmines between us. This hotch-potch of semantic mayhem became even more complicated when he phoned his girlfriend and insisted that I have a good old chin-wag with her on the tiny screen, interpreting for this, his non-English-speaking beauty. A good half hour went by before another friend arrived on a similar bike to drop me back to my little hotel in the old city. This pick-up had been arranged unbeknownst to me in yet another gesture of Iranian hospitality in a flurry of messages sent from my young friend's phone. Lazing on my hotel bed later that evening, my phone buzzed, and I saw a message from an unknown number. Obviously from the country code it was from an Iranian phone, but the message left me perplexed. *D'fhág tú do spéaclaí gréine*. Translated from Irish as 'You left your sun glasses'. Good old Google Translate.

Ten days into my travels in Iran and I was having one of those rare days when I just felt jaded with the whole sightseeing malarky. If another smiling 'tour guide' tried to convince me to see some ruin or other, I was going to 'bate the head 'of 'im', as we say in Ireland. (Do not be alarmed dear reader, we are not a violent race unless provoked). Then along came Dariush. Of a similar age to me, Dariush, was a few years into his training to become an architect. Like other tour guides, he asked me if I would be interested in a tour of Persepolis, renowned 2,500-year-old ruined Persian city, situated about 60km from Shiraz. Unlike other tour guides however, he was a quiet, unassuming man and seemed almost embarrassed to be bothering me. There was something about this man's kind and gentle attitude that made me stop and take the time to listen to him. Looking a little older than your average 44-year-old, something told me that Dariush had experienced a hard life. There was sorrow in his eyes, a wealth of pained experience and a sharp intelligence. He told me that if I was free right there and then, he would give me a tour of Shiraz's citadel *de gratis* and if, after the experience, I felt that it had been an informative and satisfying tour, I could decide if I wanted to avail of his services to visit Persepolis the next day. Walking around the citadel, Dariush explained that it was built during the Zand Dynasty by its ruler, Karim Khan Zand (reign

1751-1779). Resembling a medieval fortress, this impressive palace was the ruler's living quarters. Khan was known for his kind and gentle ways and his reign was an exceptionally peaceful one. Walking around the complex, Dariush pointed out the intricately carved ceilings, architraves as well as vibrantly coloured windows. Within the palatial hammam, stunning emerald green marble decorated the surfaces and at ceiling height the *passage du chats* allowed noxious gases to escape, in case one let a royal rip! Walking from one beautiful building to the next and listening to Dariush breathing life into the 18th century complex, what was becoming clear to me was the considerable influence that the Persian Empire had on subsequent civilisations. Its impact on Roman architecture, in the fields of medicine and mathematics and many other subjects was immense. What was also evident to me was that I had found myself one heck of a tour guide. This man was incredibly passionate about Persian history and culture and his knowledge was vast. I was going to Persepolis with Dariush and no mistake.

Picked up from my hostel at 7am the next day by Dariush and his sister Fatemeh, our friendly taxi driver, we stopped off at a bakery in downtown Shiraz to pick up some bread. Before leaving the city, we pulled up beside a busy road near the Quaran Gate. Dariush announced that we would have our breakfast here. Putting down a mat for us to sit on, we sat in a little lay-by close to the busy road. Cars beeping, fumes heavy in the early morning air, we tucked into a veritable feast, before packing up and hitting the road for the hour long journey to the ancient ruined city of Persepolis. Within a few minutes of leaving the city, I noticed Fatemeh pulling down her head scarf to reveal her beautiful chestnut coloured hair. It was obvious that she felt more at ease outside the city and its all-seeing eyes. It was also clear that brother and sister were good friends and had a mutual respect for each other. Fatemeh, like the majority of Iranians I met, spoke good English, and was clearly a very intelligent and well-educated woman. After school, she had gone on to study Chemistry at university. On graduating, she had worked as a hair stylist and also in confectionary. Like her brother and so many of their country men and women, the regime had thwarted any opportunity to make use of her academic achievement, one means by which it represses its people. Parking some distance from the UNESCO site, myself and Dariush headed off with hats, water and suncream at the ready. Even at 9am, the sun was beginning to beat down on the vast ancient city before us. Climbing magnificent steps into the Apadana Palace, with its porticos directed in three different directions, these entrances had welcomed subjects from every region of the great empire to pay homage to its rulers. Although the city had many kings during its history, the most renowned included Darius and Xerxes, bas reliefs of whom now decorate impressive door jambs to some of the palatial buildings. Just imagining the 20-metre-high columns, I pictured dignitaries waiting, tense and excited, to receive word that they could approach the mighty king. The steps adorned with bas-reliefs, depict subjects from the 23 countries of the Persian empire. These included Ethiopians, Armenians, Egyptians, Turks and a great number of tribes across ancient Iran. The ancient ceremonial city was built around 518 BC by paid employees, who were remunerated in coinage, wine and food. An advanced civilised society, ancient Persepolis, unlike most other ancient cities, was not built upon slavery, and women were held in the highest regard within society. As a testament to this, climbing the imposing steps into the now derelict palace, Dariush stopped and pointed out the figure of a woman at the axis of a large wheel. At the centre of creation was woman, the giver of life, the bearer of all that was and was to come. This was an advanced society, unique in the ancient world and some might say absent in our own time.

The following day, I was heading to the Zagros mountains for a 3-day guided hike, with my very own personal guide Koorush, a very pleasant 27-year-old Nomad from the

Lorish tribe. Unlike your typical tourist destination, you can be fortunate in countries like Iran to have a guide all to yourself. Somewhat on occasion, I have taken chances when traveling, which luckily did not get me into too much bother. In times past I might have headed off to remote places on my own, but fortunately I had heard a tale of two of unfortunate Germans who had got themselves into a bit of trouble in the mountains only weeks before my departure. Extending over 1600 km and originating in north-western Iran, the Zagros mountains follow the country's western border, crossing into south-eastern Turkey and north-eastern Iraq, and this is exactly where these lads unwittingly ended up. At 4500 metres, and without any obvious border markings, it was an easy enough mistake to wander innocently into Iran's troubled neighbour. Unfortunately, the Iraqi authorities did not look upon this kindly, and the boys ended up receiving a custodial sentence of two years, or was it two months or two days? It is after all, quite likely an urban myth, but I was taking no chances. Always up for making new friends, I was sure as hell not up for becoming besties with a lonely, sex-starved Iraqi in 51 degrees heat in a tiny, dank cell.

Two hours into the trek, having passed fluorescent green streams and waterfalls, we reached a remote mountain village. There to greet us were clucking hens, baby chicks, a horse with colourful tassels and children of all sizes, who spied us from dark doorways. On the mud rooftops walnuts were left to dry, the extracted dyes of which were used to colour carpets made by the village women. Koorush invited me into one family home for a prepared lunch. Accompanying wandering loners like myself every couple of weeks in this largely inaccessible region of the country (a 'road' had been built only in the last couple of years, which connected it to a far-flung neighbouring village), he knew the family well. We sat on the floor and watched, as little children of all sizes darted past us, the less shy ones smiling beautiful big smiles. What a sight I must have been to behold, an odd-looking man with funny coloured hair and very pale skin. What did they imagine of me, God only knows. Inhabiting the lower part of the family home, cows and other animals called to us from below. No furniture to speak of, just a few cushions lined the walls and simple rugs covered the floor. A couple of family photos decorated the unpainted walls. The woman of the house was striking. Her face spoke of a tough life of survival and hard-work, rearing her nine children. She was incredibly beautiful. Tall, strong, with jet black hair partly covered in a satin, emerald green headdress, she squatted effortlessly with trays of food. It was in these same mountains that the ancestors of modern Iranians, Syrians and Iraqis domesticated wheat, barley, pomegranates, and later, pistachios and almonds. My meal that day was a simple one of various fruits including apricots, plums, walnuts, and acorns.

Munching away on my tasty lunch, my attention was soon drawn to the man of the house, who had come into the room and knelt on a mat in the corner and had begun to pray. With his eyes shut in graceful devotion, he lowered his head to the ground and softly sent his prayers heavenward. One too many prunes, my attention was now squarely focused on my own inner rumblings, so I decided a visit to the bathroom was called for. Lowering myself to the 'squat toilet', I prayed to Allah that the man singing his prayers outside the door might instead decide to belt out a Pavarotti while I completed my ablutions. Despite having travelled a good deal in the Middle East, I still inwardly panic and close my eyes when I attempt to balance myself over these pungent portals to hell. My prayers went unanswered, alas, but within a few minutes we had headed off, having thanked our incurious but not inhospitable hosts. I spent the next two days traversing beautiful, yet unforgiving, landscapes but relished every moment as I knew all too soon, I would be on the road once more.

Towards the end of my stay in Iran, I took a night bus from Shiraz and headed to Bandar Abbas on the Persian Gulf. From there I caught a boat across to Hormoz Island, just eight kilometres off the mainland. Due to the extreme highs in temperature and the lack of precipitation, the soil and water on the island are mineral-rich. The high concentration of iron oxide in the soil gives the island a characteristic reddish hue. Even the surrounding seas are tinged with pink. Landing on the island, I felt incredibly uncomfortable, as it was so hot and humid. This was not helped by very enthusiastic *would-sell-their-granny* tuk-tuk drivers with extremely annoying horns, who spotted this ginger-headed alien a mile off. My stubborn 'they're not going to swindle me' attitude however saw me purposefully and haughtily march to the town centre (in a circuitous fashion it has to be said!)

An hour later, having had no success finding my booked homestay, I finally succumbed to the shrill beeping of a passing tuk-tuk. The driver, who had probably already passed me up and down the road a dozen times, almost collided with an unfortunate hen, as he did a 360 turn. 'Where you want to go Sir? Island tour, fish market?'. Weary, dehydrated and defeated, I showed him the address of my homestay. Possibly within 30 seconds, we careered around a corner and flew up a dusty alley and stopped outside a metal gate. Banging on the gate, there was no answer. He took out his phone and rang someone. 'Lady gone to Tehran yesterday. Husband sick'. I tried and failed miserably to explain that I had only emailed her this morning and she was waiting for me. Despite my protestations, he rang other friends, who corroborated his story. Exhausted and unable to plea my case in Farsi, I gave in and asked if he knew of any other guesthouse. 'You can stay at my home. My wife cook for you and I give you tour of Hormoz.' I knew fine well he had given me a tall story, but I decided to give in. I decided to play him at his own game. When he asked what I had been quoted for the homestay I had booked, I halved the amount and he lowered it by 30,000 Tomans, the equivalent of around £5. No one messes with The Ginge.

A few hours later, having devoured a plate of Chelo Mahi (fried fish on rice), we were in his little tuk-tuk, trundling our way out of the small town towards the Valley of the Statues. Hormuz Island emerged from the sea some 50,000 years ago, so the rocks in this ancient valley have been dramatically sculpted into strange shapes by the elements over this time period. Dragons, birds; mythical creatures all lurk around hidden corners. 600-million-year-old sedimentary rocks inlayed with volcanic materials envelop me in perfect silence. As I walk alone, dwarfed by towering canyons of vertebral column-shaped structures, I spy a little bird sat on an ancient well, hewn out of the surrounding rock. Solitary and free, it flits happily from crevice to peak. Lost in her beautiful dance, I am soon drawn from my reverie. I hear a melody, haunting and otherworldly. It ebbs and flows, but it draws me, and I begin to follow this spellbinding refrain, walking my way down narrow passageways, through a labyrinth of stone. It becomes louder and more haunting and pulls me to its source. Unexpectedly, I emerge on to a lofty outcrop of rock, perched high above a vast and majestic ocean before me. Three men sit precariously on a ledge, the sun dying in an ochre and spacious sky. The ocean bellows below. One of the men sings so hauntingly, words which my brain cannot fathom, yet my heart seems to comprehend. This is a moment in life that will stay with me until I am an old man. It reminds me of how lucky I am to be alive on this small but achingly beautiful planet. Iran gave me all of this. Its lovely kind people, its history and its charm. I am indeed the luckiest of gingers!

Hormuz Island, Persian Gulf, Iran September 2019

Interlude 1.3: On Waking

Heart quivering

Swirling inwards

Sharpest and tender-sweet ache

A memory of a deep and soulful love

Drawing of the purest truth

Complexity simplified by slumber

Truth to be heard

To be tended

A round peg in a square hole

An unfair ask

Tend to these quivering, swirling heartaches

Love. Self-compassion

No one else can mend these wounds

Love. Tend to yourself

In time, it will come

Love

A Long and Winding Road

UKHIMATH. THE NAME of this tiny mountain village in remote northern India still sends a shiver down my spine, and will be forever lodged in a cluster of neurons in the outback of my cerebral hemispheres. Which hemisphere I'm not too sure, but perhaps have a peek into my left ear and a gawk over my Corpus Callosum (please feel free) and you might just see, in the far distance beyond a long meandering neuronal highway, a faulty and flickering neon sign, welcoming you to 'Unforgettable Ukhimath' and ain't that the truth.

Having arrived in India a week before, I was determined, come what may, to trek and explore the mountains of the northern state of Uttarakhand. Bordering Tibet to the north and Nepal to the east, this immense area is home to large areas of the Himalayas and is home to the second highest peak in India, Nanda Devi (7,816m). Uttarakhand also boasts being the source of the mighty Ganges (2,601km), which originates from the Gangotri Glacier in the western Himalayas. A world away from the crazy, chaotic, and cluttered cities that we all associate with India, Uttarakhand is considered a region of outstanding beauty in this vast country. Indians frequently refer to it as Devabhumi, which translates as Land of the Gods, on account of the vast number of Hindu temples and pilgrimage sites found in the state. Keen to explore the region, I made a speedy exit from New Delhi airport and began to make my way northwards towards Haridwar, one of the larger towns in Uttarakhand. I spent two lovely days in the town, staying at a homestay with a local Indian family. Chatty, kind, warm and witty, Seema and her clan welcomed me with unbridled Indian generosity into their home, like a ginger Irish prodigal son. 'Don't be slaughtering any goats now Seema, vegetarian is just the ticket for me thanks. (Warning, dear reader. If you are ever in this amazing country, just have a look out of your minibus window as it rides past hanging, fly-infested bluish-grey cuts of meat, and you will never again look at a creature on four legs in the same way.)

Mealtimes however, were a joy as I ate delicious home-cooked dishes and enjoyed intelligent, fascinating conversation with Seema, her mother-in-law Indira (a retired teacher and force of nature) and Seema's son UV, an enthusiastic 17-year-old, full of confidence and wonder at the world he was about to step into. One of my minor missions while in Haridwar was to dye a pair of cream-coloured linen pants that had sustained a nasty oil spill. Trivial, you might say, but throwing away these trusty pants was not up for discussion. When it's in the high 30s, knocking on 40 degrees, and you have fair European skin like mine, you grow attached

to your pants (not literally, I may add, well maybe sometimes).
So it was, Seema jotted down in Hindi the name of the dyer's
stall, which I was to hand to my rickshaw driver. An economist
at heart, the lovely Seema was determined that my stay in
Haridwar would be an authentic, exciting and inexpensive
experience and insisted that I flag down a 'shared' rickshaw,
which I promptly did, and climbed in with two fellow
passengers. Indian people are perhaps the most smiley people
on the planet. There is simply nothing quite as magical as an
Indian smile. It disarms and enchants in milliseconds and as
for that endearing head swivel, well, you will be hard pressed
not to find yourself beaming ear to ear. Our rickshaw flies
through the crowded evening streets, all brightly lit and
chaotically noisy. Mopeds and hand-held carts appear at every
conceivable corner, while dogs, cows and chickens (hanging
by their legs) flash before us. Swathes of silks in saffron,
emerald greens, and iridescent blues dance. I beam a smile at
a passer-by and catch a friendly question, 'From what
country?' With beeping to beat the band and friendly corner-
stall banter, with locals engaging in deep conversation, fixing
prices, or perhaps deriding local politicians; all of this is India,
in its beautifully chaotic and enchanting way.

So it was, I was delivered to a stall, outside which sat
three friendly young men, one plunging material into a dirty

bucket. With not a word of Hindi or a word of English between us, I showed him my trusty trousers and picked a colour from his display. A half hour later and 30 rupees poorer (about 30 cents), I thanked my new friend and wandered happily off down the street with my 'new' green linen pants, narrowly avoiding my toes being squished by a passing scooter, ferrying its smiling driver with a beautifully dressed woman on side-saddle holding an incredibly cute baby. This was crazy, chaotic, but captivating India.

The plumbing in India is, however, anything but captivating. Seema's bathroom suite had every conceivable faucet and sprinkler known to man (with sparkly lights), none of which I could operate. A scalding dribble was about all I could summon from the murky depths and as for an effective toilet flush, forget it. As far as Seema's bathroom was concerned, it was a case of all fur and no knickers. Give me a bog-standard (excuse the pun!) toilet and simple no-nonsense sink any day of the week. With its record for gastroenteritis, if there was ever a country which needed fully functioning plumbing and sewage, it is India. After a heartfelt farewell, I took my leave from Seema's beautiful home and took a rickshaw to the nearest bus station. Perhaps 'station' is stretching it a bit but rather a random collection of buses. I have always loved the word 'entropy', meaning organised chaos. This is most certainly a fitting description for the transport system in India, but love it you must.

Within minutes, without requesting any help, my rucksack was vaulted on to the roof (you just hope for the best!) and I was amicably bundled (and probably fondled) on to the already packed minibus. If this were any European country, you might sigh in disappointment and trundle back down the aisle but not in India. Having made my way to the very back of the bus, an already crammed seat of students, smiled broadly, bunched up and made room for me. At six foot and about 13 stone, I inhaled deeply, smiled warmly and squeezed into what would be my space for the next five hours. Teenagers in India overflow with charm, friendliness and enthusiasm. All students who had travelled overnight from their home village to return to college to start the new term, they were 'energetic' to put it mildly, but chatting to them was a welcome distraction from the increasingly windy, bumpy mountain roads on which we soon found ourselves. Due to a pile-up on the mountainside (motorists in front trying to edge around a recent landslide), we came to an enforced, but welcome, stop and stretched our legs. Standing by a sheer drop, which overlooked the river valley far below, I was told the river was none other than the holy Ganges. I stood in awe as the mighty river arched her way through the fertile valleys below.

After a little lunch further up the road, we trundled on to my first transfer stop of Rudraprayag. The man from the campsite, where I would be staying that night, had said I should be able to catch a connecting bus from there to Ukhimath and then on to Chopta Meadows where they were based. With no concept of the distances and durations between these rural towns, I was conscious it was almost evening, and I was still a few hours from my destination. From the few locals I spoke to, it was clear that few drove in these parts once it got dark. With my ridiculously heavy rucksack on my back, I found an official looking man and asked when the next bus to Ukhimath might arrive. He pointed across the street and said, 'maybe later'. I was not filled with confidence. One or two local taxi men, spotting this pale, gormless European wandering up and down the street, quoted me their full year's wages to get me to Ukhimath. Stubborn by nature, I politely but emphatically declined, insisting I would rather wait for the bus. Two hours later, with still no sign of the bus, I was beginning to worry, and questioned my wisdom of sending the taxis away, which had long since departed. Much to my relief two young local lads arrived and said they were taking the bus heading for Ukhimath and within a few minutes it pulled up.

Once again sitting down at the very back of the bus, I chatted with the two young lads as they made their way to play football. As time went on, the road became increasingly tortuous and potholed. In some countries worsening road conditions and increasing darkness would incline a driver to perhaps slow down and drive with a little more caution, but this was India. If anything, we had the Michael Schumacher of bus drivers at the helm and within a half an hour, sitting on the back seat, I was getting used to intermittently ricocheting towards the ceiling. It was at the same time hilariously funny and vomit-inducing. I decided to try various strategies to keep the contents of my stomach exactly where they were. Eyes open, eyes closed, sitting up and lying down, deep breaths and ignoring breathing altogether. *'What an intricately designed antimacassar'* I thought to myself. Anything to distract myself from the vaulting vomitus within. I then moved to the empty seats in the middle of the bus which made absolutely no difference. Having no idea how far we were from Ukhimath, I told myself it could be no more than a couple of hours. Four hours later, as we spun around corners, hopped into and out of crater-like potholes on roads that made the lunar surface look like an ice rink, I was reconciled to the fact that it might be Christmas 2025 by the time we arrived in Ukhimath. I gripped the headrest in front of me, cursed at the driver under my breath, laughed as I bounced, willing myself repeatedly not to vomit. I tried to distract myself from thinking about what exactly I could vomit into if it came to it, but just told myself this just was not going to happen. Thankfully, we eventually meandered our way down towards a well-lit little village and came to a sudden stop on the main street. Despite the wobbly legs, I can tell you, I hopped off that bus like a spring lamb.

By the next morning, like childbirth (I imagine), I had put the experience out of my head and cheerfully jumped into the passenger seat of a shared jeep to head up into the mountains. In daylight, the beauty of this place was spellbinding. We edged around narrow mountain roads. With my window down I inhaled the crisp, fresh air, while boundless natural beauty hijacked my senses. I was completely in the moment, every care and concern relegated to the outskirts of my consciousness. We drove alongside deep, dark pine forests, with vast blue skies overhead and lush green meadows far below. Hopping out at my campsite at Chopta Meadows, I realised this would indeed be a real solo adventure, as the only staff were two local lads, neither of whom spoke any English. Chopta is a small, forested area in the larger Kedarnath Wildlife Sanctuary. Himalayan tree species include oak, pine, burans, and others which occupy most of the land. Also called Kedarnath Musk Deer Sanctuary, the area is a designated protected area for endangered Himalayan musk deer. It is also home to Himalayan Thar, Griffon, Black bear, and the much-feared Snow leopard. Oblivious at the time that I, Homo Gingus Hibernicus, could myself be an endangered species by teatime and dragged away and buried by a scary predator, I packed my little man bag with the necessary provisions and headed off with my trusty stick towards Tungnath National Park.

Heading off up the road, feeling free as a bird of paradise, this place was worth every wave of nausea that had carried me here. Ten minutes later, I stopped and took in the pristine beauty around me. This was the rural trekking I had sought, with the smell of pine trees, the sound of birdsong and the gurgle of freshwater streams. Had I listened a little more carefully, I might have heard the panting of a fiendishly ravenous snow leopard eyeing up my juicy Irish calves from the adjacent wooded inclines. Ignorant to this possibility, I was in my element and had eyes only for the vast blue sky stretching out before me, feeling gratitude wash over me like the surrounding hillside rivulets.

I paid the entrance fee at the Kedarnath National Park office and started my ascent. Strangely, the surrounding landscape put me in mind of Yorkshire, with its stone walls, ancient farm outhouses in ruins and sweeping meadows. There were very few people on the path as I made my ascent and soon it started to sleet. By the time I had climbed the steep three kilometres to Tunganath Temple it was snowing heavily. The temple is the highest shrine in the world dedicated to Lord Shiva, one of the principal deities of Hinduism. At an altitude of 3,680m, this small unassuming stone temple is thought to be at least 1000 years old. As is customary of many religions in Asia, it is expected that you remove your footwear when entering a Hindu temple and its surrounds. By this time, there was an all-out blizzard, but nonetheless I removed my walking boots and socks and stepped on the ice-cold slabs and hurried my way towards the tiny stone entrance. Once inside, I was welcomed by a holy man who blessed me, placed tilak on my forehead and guided me through a short ritual to show respect to Lord Shiva. A tilak is a red dot of vermillion paste placed between the eyebrows, an area which Hindus consider to be the locus of the third or spiritual eye, the centre of latent wisdom and concentration. Trying my best to listen attentively, my host proceeded to point out various deities within the humble, candle-lit shrine. I must say it was a very beautiful experience and I was struck by the man's devotion to stand here in the biting cold welcoming the rare visitor or trekker who trundled their way past this remote peak. Once it had stopped snowing and the sun re-emerged, I continued the ascent towards Chandrashila (meaning 'moon rock'), a peak at 4200m with spectacular views of the Himalayas. Legend has it that Lord Rama meditated here, after defeating the demon-king Ravana. I am sure he also had a bit of a shindig to celebrate. I'd say the old meditation was just to settle the headache after the night before. Unlike Lord Rama, I decided not to hang around, as I was acutely aware that the weather could change quickly, so I made my descent and arrived back at the campsite two hours later, just as it was getting dark. Sat in my tent with my woolly hat, gloves, scarf, and coat on, I attempted to write my journal, but the shivering rendered the words a spidery mess. As my thoughts turned to what else I could do before grub, one of the young chaps managing the campsite called me for dinner. The meal, consisting of homemade curry, dahl and chapatti prepared over a wood fire, was one of the tastiest I had when in India.

After a good night's sleep, I decided to trek to Deoria Tal Lake, which is located two kilometres from the pretty village of Sari at a height of 2,400 metres. So off I set on the quiet road in the direction of my destination, some 10 miles away. Accompanied by a nervous cow for the first kilometre, we parted ways and again it was just me and the surrounding woodland. Out of nowhere I heard a motorbike and the chap asked if I wanted a lift, so I climbed on the back as we freewheeled down towards the main road. Saying goodbye, I headed on to the village of Sari, from where my guidebook informed me that I could climb a series of steps up to the lake. Following a lunch in a quiet little cafe, I took the zig-zag path up to the lake which was much smaller than I expected, but very peaceful. Apart from bumping into a few cows on my way down, I became aware of singing and an accompanying drum somewhere in the valley below. As I got closer, it was obvious it was coming from a temple close to the village. Removing my shoes and socks, I walked across the grass and sat on a wall outside and listened to the mesmerising singing. Eventually I pulled myself away and started to make my way back as I had 10 miles to cover. The roads were deadly quiet with just the odd motorbike or passing van. Perhaps only halfway back, it was clear I was running out of daylight as the sun was beginning to set behind the mountains. After another mile or so, I came across a small 'café' out in the middle of nowhere, within which sat a group of young Indian friends. I sat with them and had a beer and nuts and we got into great conversation.

As time went on, I realised that they were stoned as well as being somewhat *ar meisce* (Gaelic for drunk). I excused myself as I was concerned, I might be walking in the pitch-black. One of the gang told me I was crazy to be walking in the dark, as the national park was known for its wild and not particularly friendly animals, and that he would happily give me a lift as far as the campsite. Rather unsteady on his feet, I was weighing up whether I wanted to be mauled to death by a snow leopard or to be vaulted off the back of a motorbike breaking my neck. I went for the latter. As we swerved around corners, I gripped on tightly to my friend's shoulders. It was quite disconcerting, as he frequently would turn his head right around to reassure me, his bike veering right and left undecidedly. 'It's okay my friend. Would I put you in any danger?' Trying to laugh this off and encouraging him to look at the road ahead, it was a massive relief to get to the campsite in one piece. I think, in retrospect, I might have taken my chances with the snow leopard.

Leaving the campsite at dawn the next day, I heaved my rucksack on to my back and set off on the road again. I knew at this stage, judging from the terrain and my map, that getting to my next destination by evening would be a challenge, however it was a challenge I embraced. Within a half hour, much to my relief, a car slowed up and a young Indian couple, who had been at my campsite, told me to jump in. They discussed how proud they were of their country and the fact that India was unique in having maintained its identity and culture, despite occupation by the Portuguese, the British and Persian Empires as well as Afghanistan. The Portuguese, for instance, opened sea lanes around the Cape of Good Hope on Africa's southernmost tip in 1488, after which they had direct access to Asia and established themselves in India in 1505. Incredibly, Portugal still governed parts of India until 1961. The British, on the other hand, arrived in 1757 with just 3,000 soldiers from the British East India Company and defeated the Nawab (Duke) of Bengal and his 50,000-strong army. Heavy rains had ruined the quality of the Nawab's gunpowder. Up until then, the British East India Company had traded primarily in silk, cotton, tea, and opium, but having laid claim to vast areas of the country, they now functioned as the military authority in large sections of India. Negotiating potholes and landslides, my Indian friends told me how the British had, under Queen Victoria, sought to 'better' its Indian subjects. In effect this meant obliterating cultural practices and educating the Indian people to think with a British mind set. I could sense the anger and sadness as the young woman in the front expressed the grievances of a nation. It was not until 1947 that the British left but not before partitioning the province of Bengal into the predominantly Hindu West Bengal (under India) and the predominantly Muslim East Bengal (now Bangladesh). The latter became a province of Pakistan and the overall result of this set Muslim against Hindu and sadly the tensions have only escalated in recent years.

Thus, the conversation ran and after three hours' drive, they dropped me off in the small town of Srinagar where I would catch a bus to Kanatal. For the first time since I arrived, the cultural norms began to really get on my goat. For a start there was nobody at the bus office and no one seated outside. It seemed entirely unsure as to whether there *would* indeed be a bus to Kanatal that day or *ever* for that matter! I would say though, that I was the first ginger-haired Irishman to ever set foot in the place. Everyone seemed to be staring at me. Even a passing cow meandering down the moped-mobbed street, stopped, turned its head in my direction and gave me a good old stare. 'Feck off cow' I telepathically communicated. When the bus arrived, I could have kissed that flippin' cow and I climbed on board, my spirits raised, but after the first hour, as the bus bumped and wound its way around hairpin mountain roads, I began to feel waves of nausea and impatience building once more. Lying down on the back seat, window open, staring at the beautiful sky as it sped by, I breathed deeply and prided myself for not having eaten a morsel all day, quite insistent that I would not disgrace myself. Three hours later, and a good deal greener in complexion, I vowed to never complain about the Irish transport system ever again as I jumped off the bus, and thanked the bus maniac, I mean, driver.

Three minibus rides later, I alighted at the entrance to NamaStay EcoHostel, and it was well worth the day's journey. A quiet, peaceful location with views of the mountains, the hostel was simple but beautifully maintained. Yudhish, the manager was a handsome, gentle and wise chap in his mid-30s. He exuded calm and just to be in his presence was a tonic. He had completed two ten-day Vipassana retreats, was a yoga teacher and had recently done a Zen meditation course. 'Run for president why don't you? You've done everything else for Shiva's sake!' I thought. Vipassana is the meditation technique the Buddha practised over two and a half millennia ago, while Zen, he explained was the Japanese interpretation of Dhyana, the Hindu word for meditation, as taught by the Buddha. During our chats, he would tell me how important it was to be aware of what we consume in terms of our body and mind. 'Easier said than done Yudhish, my man, but you're dead right!' I went for walks during the day, read and did a bit of yoga with Yudhish and thoroughly enjoyed the food he prepared. I even had a go on a sitar. My stay there was nourishing in every sense of the word, and I left a couple of days later, completely at ease and at peace with myself and the world.

Whizzing along on the back of a motorbike, we descended the long and winding road into Chamba, with pine forests on one side and beautiful countryside rolling to the horizon on the other. To not hold on tightly to this rather strapping man would have been pure negligence from a road safety point of view, and meandering along the snaking forested inclines of northern India in the open air, I had to ask myself, 'Does life get better than this?'

Making sure I got into the correct jeep that would take me close to Dehradun airport, I lodged myself in the back of the spacious vehicle, that is, four people to the four seats, as opposed to the usual six to four ratios. On the inevitably bumpy and high-speed journey along steep rock faces which had experienced recent landfalls, the elderly man opposite me proceeded to feel my ginger, hairy legs in full view of his wife and the other passengers sitting down the rear. Initially taken aback, I soon realised it was mere curiosity at this ginger creature opposite him. His wife, with other things on her mind, wound down the window, stuck her head out and was sick. I am hoping it wasn't my ginger legs or her hubby's unusual behaviour that upset her delicate entrails. In hindsight, I put all this down to cultural norms. Entrails aside, I do love that about India; the way these people teach us so much about our western hang-ups, expectations, and intolerance. She wound the window back up and continued with her knitting.

After a fond farewell to my new boyfriend, his wife and the other passengers, I jumped out of the back of the jeep, crossed the road, as fast as my ginger legs could take me, and began walking the short two kilometres to the small airport of Dehradun. Beautiful pink blossoms on the trees were intensified by a backdrop of a vast blue sky. I beamed and just thought 'this is the life!'

Seema and her mother-in-law Indira, my hosts in Haridwar

Chandrisilla (4.200m), Kadernath Sanctuary

Small Hindu temple near Sari Village

Tales of the Unenlightened

IN OCTOBER 2019, I found myself in a rickshaw heading out of the small city of Jodhpur, in the Indian desert state of Rajasthan. My driver was a cantankerous young man, with a bit of an attitude. Having signed up for a Vipassana ten-day silent meditation retreat, I myself was on the edge of the edge. I had been in India about two weeks and had thoroughly enjoyed the experience for the most part. Having been incredibly moved by the beauty of the Taj Mahal, I then headed to the northern town of Haridwar on the holy Ganges, where I experienced the beautiful nightly *Ganga Aarti*, a ceremony where Hindus congregate, say prayers and release candles down the sacred river, all this to the beating of cymbals and donging of bells. A few days later, a torturous day-long minibus journey on potholed 'roads', complete with fellow passengers vomiting out of the windows in the crowded bus, brought me to a beautiful pristine mountainous region in the northern state of Uttarakhand. Hiking solo for a few days with only the odd nervous cow to keep me company along the beautiful forest roads, the tall pines pierced the clear blue skies above. The air was so fresh and so pure that every bit of stress ebbed out of my body. A hellish nine-hour train journey a few days later, from Jaipur to Jodhpur, put paid to that. With standing room only, I consciously blocked my nose as I stood in the cramped passageway between carriages, right outside the toilet, where little fleas meandered excitedly at its vent in anticipation of the delights within. Stopping between stations for an immeasurable amount of time, with a scowling expression to beat the band, this grumpy western tourist marched down the platform to find another carriage. This just wouldn't do! Here I found an empty first-class berth, 'first' being the last word I would use to describe the carriage, however it was the lap of luxury to me; this tiny bit of space to call my own without the stench of urine. Normally I am not a grumpy individual, so when the guilt abated, I began to relax. Sadly, this was short lived, as a conductor found me out and with an air of satisfaction charged me for the privilege of moving to another carriage. On arrival in Jodhpur, I felt quite exhausted by the experience and could not yet see the bright side of my trip. I was beginning to doubt whether I was in the best state of mind to head into a no-nonsense meditation retreat.

Anyway, back to my rickshaw driver. Despite my initial polite and then insistent pleas to phone the meditation centre, he insisted he knew where he was going, stopping every so often to shout into his phone, clearly outraged that the local county council had obviously reconfigured the entire road system overnight, without consulting him first. Eventually, in a very stressed state, we arrived at the gates of the Vipassana Centre, Jodhpur. For those of you unfamiliar with the term, Vipassana is said to be the original meditation 'method' the historical Buddha practised over two and a half millennia ago. None of your fancy incense sticks and flowing yoga movements, this was the hard-core stuff: sitting for one to two hour stretches without moving a muscle in complete and uninterrupted silence. Banging the door of the rickshaw (well actually, this is what I would have done if rickshaws had doors), I said a curt goodbye to my 'friend' and turned on my heels, with a 'that showed him' attitude, and made my way to the building. The entrance itself was unimposing, almost inviting in fact, with a courtyard beyond, edged with greenery. Inviting, was certainly not high on the agenda of the staff seated at the registration desk. Met by two rather brusque, sombre gentlemen seated at the desk and another kindlier individual, I felt that perhaps I had stumbled into a panel interview for Indian Rail. It was chaotic, bureaucratic, and involved a lot of form filling, photocopying and a bizarre system, whereby candidates were moved around the room randomly, like we were playing Indian musical chairs. After a bit of grilling to ensure I was aware of what was expected of course participants, I was informed in no uncertain terms that

I would be residing in cell B8, Block B, which immediately sent shivers up my not-as-yet aching spine. An hour later, twenty-five quivering, pale participants sat in an unventilated room, listening to a rather dour, balding monotonous living cadaver. *'Good Jaysus, I hope to God he's not the flippin' teacher'*, I thought to myself. In a thick Indian accent, he proceeded to outline the dos and don'ts of camp life, with that endearing little oscillating head tilt unique to the Indian nation. 'No one is permitted to leave the site for the duration of the course. Women and men will be segregated and there will be absolutely no talking allowed. You will hand in all reading and writing materials as well as your mobile phone at 4.30pm today. If you have any doubts as to your ability to stay for the duration of the course, tell us now and you can leave'. Deathly silence ensued. This was followed by a video of a much nicer, greener, and quieter meditation centre somewhere in the US, where the narrator reiterated these same rules, but in a less threatening manner. With a knot in my stomach and *major* reservations as to what I had just signed up to, I surrendered my small bag of contraband and gulped down my trepidation.

Day One began as all the others would, with a wake-up call at 4am. Our alarm clock was a horrendous discord, issued from a mechanical bell from the distant meditation hall. To say I had the feeling that I had awoken in a cross between a Japanese Prisoner of War camp and Mountjoy Prison was an understatement. Without any communication (gesturing, verbal, eye contact), myself and my cell mate telepathically managed to instigate a routine of bathroom use. A young guy from London, recently graduated, he was very serious and was definitely compliant with camp rules. So off we trudged in the dark to the meditation hall to begin our first 4.30 to 6.30am session. Once we all got into our sitting or kneeling position of choice, silence settled across the hall for the next hour. We had been given a few guidelines the night before and were aware that the first nine days would comprise ten hours of practice, including meals, walking and rest periods. No other form of exercise or practice was permitted. In the evening, we would attend a Buddhist Dharma teaching, which was a video-recorded teaching of Buddhist psychology, given by the man who brought Vipassana out of Myanmar (Burma) to various countries, Sri Satya Narayana Goenka (try saying that with a mouthful of curry chips washed down with a diet Coke!)

For the first three days, we had been told that the sole intention was to focus our attention, by noticing sensations in the triangular area below the nostrils and above the upper lip (*Holy mother of the Divine, what the blazes had I signed up for?*) We would be given further instructions on Day Three. Anyway, back to session one. There I was, in complete silence, trying diligently to muster up or imagine sensations in my little triangle, when suddenly a horrendous discord of unintelligible utterance was issued from the overhead speakers, that almost propelled me forward on to the poor unsuspecting Indian chap in front. This cacophony was to become a staple of all the meditation sessions, which we subsequently learned were the beautiful teachings of the Buddha from 2,500 years previous, but delivered in a very disturbing demonic-sounding chant in the ancient Pali language. To my virgin ears, I thought old Buddha had flung open his coffin and was announcing in gravelly discords his vengeful return. Physically, by the end of the first day, having sat for what seemed like nine and a half weeks, I was near to tears. With utter disbelief, and not a little envy, I opened my eyes and took the odd sneaky little peek at my fellow participants. Mostly Indian, the majority of them sat effortlessly, with knees crossed right under their shins and their thighs in full contact with the floor. Meanwhile, my poor auld Irish legs were 'giving out good-o', and as for my poor hip muscles, they had a bit of Ian Paisley about them. 'No surrender!' they screamed in angry tones. Ever the anxious and diligent student however, I did my utmost to please the teacher within, and sit still. For me, this was a high kneeling position, where my posterior was propped up with about 16 gazillion cushions with a few blankets squeezed into anatomical nooks and crannies I didn't even know I possessed. This was in stark and embarrassing contrast to my Indian colleagues who, unlike me, sat with just an auld slip of a cushion under their flexible rear ends, if that.

Very soon, however, I got into the swing of camp life. One to two-hour blocks of meditation with five-minute interludes between them. By the third day, when I started to think *'For feck sake, can we please do some other flippin' practice apart from sitting'*, I became suddenly aware that the older French lady in our group had slumped worryingly to one side. *'Holy God, she's literally died of boredom'*. Much to my relief within a few minutes, I saw her move a little and adjust herself back to the middle. Mealtimes were nice enough, at least initially, but very soon became an exercise in tolerance and meditation themselves. Who in God's name concocted the notion of savoury rice crispies, porridge and tomato soup? This was our daily evening meal without variation. Within a few days, the predictability of each meal dulled the senses, and one became more aware of the noisy and disgusting eating habits of one's fellow participants. There was much slurping, burping, belching and wolfing down of food. One man in particular, Burpy Stinky Man, I liked to call him, really got on my goat and was met with shocking internal criticism. I saw my intolerance grow from day to day and, despite all the meditation I had done, this intolerance reigned supreme at mealtimes. Nonetheless, compassion and disgust accompanied each other in equal measures. I realised very soon that these reactions were all of my own making, internally generated. These individuals were my teachers in tolerance.

Meanwhile, back in the meditation Hall, the Indian acceptance of all bodily functional noises was brought to a whole new level. Three main culprits included Burpy Stinky Man, who would literally tilt his rear end to one side and let out a horrendous fart, with obvious pride. The second culprit, who had an uncanny resemblance to Manuel from Faulty Towers, assisted the teacher on the retreat, but spent most of his time sat at the back of the room (right beside me) cross legged, belching, clearing his throat (like Basil Brush) and breaking wind on an incredibly frequent basis. Way too much Daal obviously! The last man on my 'shit-list', who shared the same skillset as those above, was middle aged with an extremely nervy disposition. Between meditation sessions he would pace frantically from one end of the courtyard to the other repetitively, and worryingly he appeared to be having a good old chat with himself. Throughout all of this, we had occasional soundbites from (recorded) Mr. Goenka, who encouraged us to bring 'equanimity' to our experience as we traced our sensations up and down the body. He also had a penchant for repeating certain adverbs. 'Work diligently, diligently…patiently and persistently, patiently and persistently perfect equanimity, perfect equanimity'. It was a nice break from the silence however, Old Mr Goenka's voice, and I have to say I used to look forward to his dharma recordings. Attempting to focus my attention on sensations in my body, while at the same time acutely aware of my anger and intolerance for aforementioned Indian social norms, I was nearly driven to distraction. I consciously told myself every time I heard a bodily emission, these people were my teachers in tolerance but, by God, I wanted to strangle that little Manuel fella by the end of the day. Given this crazy inner reactivity to all bodily noises in my mind, coupled with the physical pain of sitting or kneeling in the one position for hour long periods, by Day Five my frustration was such that, at the end of the session, when participants would typically chant 'Sadhu, Sadhu, Sadhu', I muttered under my breath 'Fuck you, Fuck you, Fuck you'. The repetitive meditation techniques, the burping, the physical pain just got too much.

Despite all of this, I must admit I worked bloody hard at it, so much so that by Day Eight I noticed, although the same triggers were present, my mind was more adept at noticing the reactivity and particularly I noticed where it was housed in my body. Instead of feeding the beasts of intolerance and rage, I tended to my suffering, the tension I was creating all by myself and this dear reader, was my balm. Often following sessions, compassion filled me with an appreciation of my physical abilities. Burpy Stinky Man limping and singing to himself (on a silent retreat?) with stains on his pants. Poor man. Like the ocean, swells of compassion and storms of internal rage battered, but softened my heart. Tears of love for my fellow man came, with acute awareness of our imperfect, beautiful and brittle nature.

On the tenth day of the retreat, we were allowed to speak to one another for the first time. In the preceding hours, I was acutely aware of a growing knot of tension in my stomach. The plain fact was that I was nervous about the whole prospect of interacting with others. I found this quite interesting because, for the first time in my life, I was fully aware of the anxiety that comes with social interaction, of which I am usually quite oblivious. Deep down I have always felt like a shy, introverted individual and in fact, for the first seven or eight years of my life, I didn't talk much at all. A primary school teacher once remarked that 'he doesn't say much but he smiles a lot'. As an adult, I am well able to chat away and others have often commented how sociable I am, but deep down I sense the anxiety hanging in the ether, but it was never so obvious to me as on this occasion. Nonetheless, when it came to it, we entered into gentle conversation in pairs or small groups, and it was just beautiful to hear and know these people in front of me. A lot of my crazy thoughts were quickly put to bed, as I met individuals with whom it had been forbidden to even really look at, up until a few minutes previously. To many, it might seem ridiculous to agree to go into complete silence, with no interaction with your fellow man, but only when that freedom is surrendered and then given back, do you know its richness. I met many beautiful souls that day including a guy whose general anatomy I fell in love with over the preceding ten days (particularly his shapely backside sitting in the Lotus position). Safe to say it wasn't Burpy Stinky Man. Then there was Goran, a lovely young German, who shared so openly about the challenges and insights he experienced over the ten days. I also met a young woman from Puerto Rica, who smiled and laughed so beautifully, I felt tears well up inside me. One by one, I got chatting to most of the twenty or so participants and rarely have I met such beautiful souls. Indian youths with such broad smiles and such positive outlooks.

Heading to the airport, I shared a rickshaw with the lovely French lady who I thought had popped her clogs towards the beginning of our collective captivity. Céline, who now lived on Réunion Island in the Seychelles, had attended five previous Vipassana courses in various countries. She was the embodiment of kindness, warmth and compassion. She had had a full and interesting life, living in various European countries including Ireland, as well as India and parts of Africa. In her early 70s now, she made jewellery and sold it just for fun. We had a lovely 'chinwag', both on our way to the airport and in its chaotic lounge. Despite being jam packed and an absence of flight monitors, I looked around at the craziness and never felt such love and compassion for my fellow man, even amid the screams of hungry, tired babies. Having said farewell to Céline, I boarded the plane to Cochin. As we taxied the runway before take-off, I cried as I looked out of the window, having just read a few lines from Goenka's book, which resonated with my own deepest conviction of many years. 'When the mind is freed of conditioning, it is always full of love and pure love. If you remove the negativity, the positivity remains, purity remains.'

The Dance

EDDIE PLACED AN imperfect but loving grip on her rather generously endowed posterior, as he smiled lovingly down at her. At a towering 6 foot 4 and she a good foot and a half shorter and wider, they beamed like bashful teenagers as they slowly and clumsily waltzed to the music set up on my phone. Not exactly qualifying material for *Strictly*, this was indeed something magical, and all of us who witnessed it, knew it. Eddie would be discharged from hospital the following day, having been an inpatient for over 4 months. He had at this point become part of our NHS furniture. As one of his treating physiotherapists on the stroke unit, my first encounter with this lovely 67-year-old gentle Scotsman was a memorable one. He was a quiet man with a lovely smile, but within a few minutes of asking him about his stroke, he sobbed like a little boy. I took his flaccid, useless hand and looked into his eyes, unable to promise anything, afraid to give hope, but told him that we would work together and that we would do our best. He told me how, in a frightening life-changing moment just a few weeks before, he had suffered a massive brain haemorrhage, which left him completely paralysed on his left side. As a neurological physiotherapist, I have assessed and moved many a limp and non-functioning limb, but these limbs had not even a flicker of activity. A leg that had walked his wife down the aisle (not on its own it must be said!), had walked his little girl to school years before, had scaffolded dirty britches, which descended the coal mines of the northeast Scottish coastline, day after long day. These same legs had danced and stumbled in the pubs and dancehalls of working-class Fife and had struggled to stabilise themselves as they followed the coffin of his lovely wife just a few years before. Eddie had eventually found love again, but his hidden and unspoken heartache had encouraged nights of excessive lone drinking, binge eating and reduced physical activity. Eventually, his body couldn't take the abuse and he paid a near ultimate price. Within our first few sessions, we would use an electrical hoist to lift this giant of a man, who now lacked the sitting balance of a toddler, into a specialised postural management chair, the equivalent of the highest-spec Jag. Supported fully on his left side, tilted 20 degrees or so back and wearing a harness, he would not be at risk of falling. In our jobs as therapists, nursing staff and doctors, we can easily become desensitised to what is before us; an adult human rendered immobile, dependent, and devastated.

My introduction to physiotherapy had started 20 years before, when I was employed as a physiotherapy assistant in Hope Hospital, Salford in Greater Manchester. I loved the job from the get-go; the teamwork, the comradery, and the diverse range of humanity that we encountered, day in and day out. As Salford has a large older Irish population, it was lovely to meet elderly men and women from my homeland. It was the work itself though, that drew me in. I knew from early on that neurology was the speciality for me. I had studied neuroscience as part of my undergraduate degree. To bear witness to the impact of a compromised nervous system and the ways in which it can be rehabilitated fascinated me. Stripped back to our most vulnerable state, we are the same, in need of care, attention, love and encouragement. Vulnerability wears many guises however ,and of course it doesn't always bring out the best in patient or 'professional', but more often than not, it does. Whatever our bank balance, the type of property we live in, the places we come from, what we have done or not done in life, we all share the same needs. As the Norwegian songstress Ane Brun puts it so beautifully, 'all we want is love'. Complexities of neurological function and dysfunction aside, or any other aspect of our physiology for that matter, this is the sustenance for which we hunger; the lifeforce that sustains us beyond our most basic bodily needs.

The death of my mother threw my own life into years of disarray and so I would, after 8 happy years in the northwest of England, eventually move back home to Ireland. Before I left however, I attended university yet again, to train to become a physiotherapist. Back on home turf, I worked in several settings, including intensive care, where I would learn to suction the bejaysus out of a pair of auld grotty lungs, and orthopaedics which bored me to tears. Musculoskeletal outpatients surprised me, in that I really enjoyed seeing most people recover. The human body has an incredible knack of healing itself. We therapists sometimes just really need to show a little concern in terms of human touch and compassion, with a lot of common sense thrown in. Time and again, though, I would return to the brainbox of them all. Neurology. I did a stint at Beaumont Hospital, which is the main centre of excellence in Ireland for all things *nasty about neurons*. Lovely staff and nice patients, but the place itself was as hectic as Dublin Airport on Christmas Eve. Poorly designed and about as conducive to rehabilitation as a stint in Alcatraz, again and again I question how on God's earth can we expect people to get better in stressful, noisy and overcrowded environments.

There is something humbling and heart rendering about kneeling at a person's feet, supporting their knee and seeing the first flickers of activity in their thigh muscles, or feeling the faintest grip of a human hand which has laid dormant for months. Unfortunately, in lots of situations, people may not recover movement or function, and as a therapist it can be down to you to deliver this most devastating of news; that this may be as good as it will get, or that perhaps home is no longer an option. Imparting such heart-breaking news kills me every time but, luckily, there are those breakthrough moments when someone takes a step and you could jump for joy with them. To bear witness to moments when sheer joy and relief flash across the human countenance is a privilege of the highest order. This is why I do what I do.

One the greatest opportunities in my career was when Dublin-based neurological physiotherapist Gráinne McKeown finally gave in to my relentless letters and emails begging her for a job. Initially I was a bit scared of the said Gráinne, as she was reputedly not to be messed with, but very soon I learned that this woman was one of the kindest and most skilled individuals I would ever know. A neurological whiz and a female dynamo to boot, this Belfast born therapist. with a sharp and endearing wit, was exactly the type of personality to whom I could truly relate. As a youngster and adolescent, I imagine like me, Gráinne never quite fitted into the cool gang, but also like me, she had a whacky side with huge potential and passion for her craft. Committed to her patients, with a wonderful sense of humour to match, a gentle and sensitive heart, I was so impressed by her attitude, enthusiasm, passion, and skill. Gráinne is one of those rare physiotherapists who is hands-on. Sadly, the physiotherapy profession is becoming more and more exercise prescription-based, with a little token fondle thrown in. Joking! (About the fondling I mean). Physiotherapy does not need to be complicated. It just requires an inquisitive mind, an objective pair of eyes, a pair of receptive and sensitive hands and a compassionate heart. Gráinne embodied this and reminded me of my own capacity, of the therapist that I can be and for this, I will always keep her in my heart and on my phone.

Never the best communicator in the world, however, my decision to move to Scotland to live a more independent life, continue to work in 'neuro' and perhaps meet a lovely Scotsman into the bargain (I didn't mention that one when I gave my notice!), was delivered with all the finesse of an articulated lorry bombing down the M50 at 120 kilometres an hour. My departure, in the midst of the ongoing COVID pandemic, did not help matters, but the very kind-hearted Ms McKeown forgave and understood me. (I do sometimes think, when interacting with me, people need to be somewhat telepathic as what comes out of my mouth when I am anxious, and tongue tied would make Stan Laurel scratch his head in bewilderment).

So, it was a few months later that I found myself standing in a staff room on a stroke unit in a small country hospital in rural Scotland with a lump in my throat, witnessing a teary-eyed Eddie, beaming from ear to ear and whispering something beautiful, no doubt, into his beloved Bertha's ear. By no means was it elegant, this waltz of theirs, but I promised him he would dance before he headed off into the next chapter of his life. These are the moments that I treasure, the moments I thank some unseen force for guiding me into this vocation. Despite the stressful times, when all your hard work sinks into failure and not a flicker of muscle activity is seen, the terrible news you never want to deliver that must be imparted, the sheer heartache of seeing the most vulnerable lose the last vestiges of understanding and insight as they ebb away forever. In spite and because of all of this, those precious moments, when the human spirit emerges to shine brighter than the brightest sun and grace reveals itself in its most beautiful dance, we must never give in, and we must always keep heart.

BV - #0006 - 190523 - C11 - 216/138/8 - PB - 9781739328603 - Gloss Lamination